Instructor's Resource Manual

Holly Frost

Anatomy & Physiology for Emergency Care

Frederic H. Martini, Ph.D.

Edwin F. Bartholomew, M.S.

Bryan E. Bledsoe, D.O., F.A.C.E.P., F.A.A.E.M., F.A.E.P., EMT-P

Emergency Care Contributions

Prentice Hall

Upper Saddle River, New Jersey 07458

Instructor's Resource Manual developed by:

Holly Frost, MS, NREMT-P
Assistant Professor and Program Head
Emergency Medical Technology Program
Northern Virginia Community College
Annandale, VA
and
Adjunct Assistant Professor
Emergency Health Services Program
The George Washington University
Washington, D.C.

Publisher: *Julie Levin Alexander*
Assistant to Publisher: *Regina Bruno*
Executive Editor: *Greg Vis*
Managing Development Editor: *Lois Berlowitz*
Development Editor: *John Joerschke*
Editorial Assistant: *Monica Silva*
Senior Marketing Manager: *Tiffany Price*
Product Information Manager: Rachele Triano
Director of Production and Manufacturing:
  Bruce Johnson
Managing Production Editor: *Patrick Walsh*
Manufacturing Buyer: *Pat Brown*
Production Liaison: *Jeanne Molenaar*
Creative Director: *Cheryl Asherman*
Cover Design Coordinator: *Maria Guglielmo*
Cover Designer: *Maria Guglielmo*
Composition: *Jeanne Molenaar*
Printing and Binding: *Banta Harrisonburg*

Pearson Education LTD.
Pearson Education Australia PTY, Limited
Pearson Education Singapore, Pte. Ltd
Pearson Education North Asia Ltd
Pearson Education Canada, Ltd.
Pearson Educación de Mexico, S.A. de C.V.
Pearson Education—Japan
Pearson Education Malaysia, Pte. Ltd
Pearson Education, Upper Saddle River, New Jersey

Notice on Care Procedures: It is the intent of the authors and publisher that this book be used as part of a formal EMS program taught by a licensed physician. The procedures described in this book are based upon consultation with EMS and medical authorities. The authors and publisher have taken care to make certain that these procedures reflect currently accepted clinical practice; however, they cannot be considered absolute recommendations.

The material in this book contains the most current information available at the time of publication. However, federal, state, and local guidelines concerning clinical practices, including, without limitation, those governing infection control and universal precautions, change rapidly. The reader should note, therefore, that the new regulations may require changes in some procedures.

It is the responsibility of the reader to familiarize himself or herself with the policies and procedures set by federal, state, and local agencies as well as the institution or agency where the reader is employed. The authors and publisher of this book disclaim any liability, loss, or risk resulting directly or indirectly from the suggested procedures and theory, from any undetected errors, or from the reader's misunderstanding of the text. It is the reader's responsibility to stay informed of any new changes or recommendations made by federal, state, or local agency as well as by his or her employing institution or agency.

Dedication

Love and thanks to Hannah, Lily, and Dan for
their support, patience, and belief in me and this
project. Thanks to my students who put up with
me, and thanks to my patients, who
have taught me to be passionate about the
wonders of the human body.

10 9 8 7 6 5 4 3 2 1
ISBN 0-13-099373-5

CONTENTS

CHAPTER 1

An Introduction to Anatomy and Physiology

INTRODUCTION

The average paramedic is passionate about saving lives, but definitely *not* passionate about learning the hard sciences. The key to teaching anatomy and physiology to these dedicated prehospital care providers is emotionally motivating them towards accepting the physiologic concepts as critical to effective patient care.

Most EMS providers begin an anatomy and physiology course intimidated by what they are about to encounter. When the first lesson immediately dives into enormous amounts of new terminology and definitions, it confirms their fears. The instructor's most important role is to ensure that the presentation of this new material will be gradual and that grasping the concepts will make the students better care providers, which is their primary reason to be there. The instructor needs to be passionate about both the topic and its application to emergency medical care. Pertinent firsthand experiences are often helpful to "rope in" students and get them to care about the adventure they are about to begin.

Hopefully, the EMT has had exposure to medical terminology prior to beginning the A&P course. If not, this will be a daunting experience. The instructor can allay these fears by showing examples of huge medical terms broken down into easily understandable pieces (for example, hemopneumothorax = blood [hemo] + air [pneumo] + inside the chest [thorax]). Encourage students to use a medical dictionary throughout their studies in order to become more comfortable with medical terminology in general. Also stress that every paramedic's worst fear is being involved in a lawsuit and that appropriate use of medical verbiage in a well-written call sheet is the best defense in such an event.

1

LECTURE NOTES AND TEACHING STRATEGIES

1. **Start slowly.** Define and explain the following terms.

    a. Anatomy—The who, what, and where of the body.

    b. Physiology—The why, when, and how of the body.

    c. Pathophysiology—When something goes wrong in the body; therefore, what the paramedic needs to understand and be able to anticipate and treat. *Pathos* means "disease"; in anatomy and physiology, this definition includes not only communicable diseases but trauma, acute and chronic disorders, and congenital defects as well.

    d. Homeostasis—The "normal" state. A lay person can easily understand that a steady state exists within the body, but the true depths of this concept are mind-boggling. Use the homeostatic examples to tie in every system of the body. This is a great tool for summarizing at the end of every lesson.

2. **Explain levels of organization**. Ask the class to name the levels or to call out ideas as to their breakdown. Since the lessons start with the most difficult concepts for the EMS provider to grasp, involve students emotionally in the process down to the molecular level. Naming the organ systems and giving broad functional descriptions as a group participation activity encourages everyone to be involved.

3. **Describe the feedback mechanisms**. Use examples to which the EMS provider can relate. For instance, use the progression from onset of labor to the delivery of a baby to illustrate positive feedback and the secretion of insulin to lower blood glucose levels to illustrate negative feedback.

4. Discuss surface anatomy terminology. Use a full-size mannequin for a group participation activity. Begin with directional terminology (anterior vs. posterior), and then go on to regional terminology (thoracic, abdominal). Emphasize that using the exact,

specific terminology is especially critical in EMS as the care provider must be the eyes, ears, and hands of their medical director. When the paramedic describes an injury over the radio, the medical director must be able to visualize it exactly. Explain that a knowledge of body cavities helps the paramedic understand why injured or ill organs cause referred or radiating pain to specific regions. The boundaries of each cavity also help the paramedic understand how various conditions develop (for example, cardiac tamponade from the heart encased in the pericardium).

CHAPTER 2

The Chemical Level Of Organization

INTRODUCTION

While the molecular level of the body seems as far removed from emergency medical services as possible, a basic knowledge of this topic is critical to the implementation of appropriate emergency medical care. Understanding the chemistry of the body will help the paramedic understand why a certain drug might be less effective as an antiarrhythmic agent due to a particular patient's underlying metabolic condition. For a trauma patient, abnormal cellular mechanics can lead to rapid decompensation in shock.. The chemistry of the body is the key to understanding interactions among all pharmacologic agents, a particularly challenging task in this exciting age of technical advances in drug therapies.

This is a difficult chapter for the EMS student to grasp, mostly due to the microscopic nature of the material. The chemical basis of life is not a topic conducive to the classic hands-on activities on which EMS education is based. The instructor's comfort with and passion for the material are critical for the EMS student to adapt to the subject.

LECTURE NOTES AND TEACHING STRATEGIES

1. **Explain atomic structure and energy concepts.**

   a. Define neutrons—Explain the dramatic advances of diagnostic imaging in nuclear medicine using radioisotopes.

   b. Define electrons—Discuss the concept of bond formation in terms familiar to the EMS student. Explain how a patient can take a pill every day, add a variety of food products, and gain consistent results as the chemical bonds are broken and reformed within the body.

c. Explain energy concepts in terms of the mechanism of injury during trauma. For example, how fast the car was going when it ran into a second car will help determine the extent of injuries based on the force with which various internal organs strike each other.

2. **Discuss chemical processes**, using digestion as an analogy.

   a. Define decomposition—The EMT eats (very quickly!) a cheeseburger on the way to a call.

   b. Define catabolism—The components of the cheeseburger are not immediately available to the body, so they are broken into useable portions.

   c. Synthesis——The byproducts of the burger are recombined to form useable products (insulin, to sustain appropriate blood sugar through the rest of the 24-hour shift, regardless of food intake).

3. **Explain acid/base.**—Draw the pH scale as a class participation activity, naming substances and determining where they fit on the scale (for example, use the components of the typical EMS diet: carbonated sodas, coffee, orange juice on an empty stomach). The incidence of peptic ulcers in the EMS population is now clearly explained!

   Note: An illustrative analogy for teaching pH is the phenomenon of aspiration pneumonia, a particularly tough outcome for the paramedics as they "win the battle, but lose the war" after a successful postarrest resuscitation. After a thorough discussion of the properties of acids, the potential destruction to the pulmonary tissue is easy to anticipate.

4. **Discuss the properties of water**. A class participation activity about various properties of water is helpful. Students do not yet understand chemistry well enough to begin to think about why so many physiologic properties are based on the aqueous milieu of the body. Further, understanding these properties helps to illuminate the need for adequate perfusion and why its support should be a pinnacle priority for all EMS providers during

patient care.

    a. Describe water as a solvent—Put this in terms of an oral medication's effectiveness depending on the tablet dissolving within the stomach and being absorbed into the plasma.

    b. Explain the high specific heat factor of water—How can the EMT work efficiently on an MVA on a sweltering hot day in July and then during a blizzard just a few months later without any loss of functioning? The specific heat index of the largely aqueous body allows for homeostasis in a varied environment.

    c. Pressure resistance—Use the real-life example of moving a ten-story section of Mile High Stadium in Denver, Colorado, on a minute layer of water.

    d. Electrolytes—Refer to familiar examples. The paramedic student who has even a rudimentary knowledge of cardiac function will remember the basics of sodium and potassium being separated by the cellular membrane. Knowledge of salts and their resulting electrolytes will now make more sense. Also, most EMS providers have an active exercise regimen, so they will be familiar with electrolyte replacement through their awareness of "sports drinks."

5. Define compounds; explain the following compounds relevant to EMS:

    a. Carbohydrates—Summarize briefly the use of glucose for energy production, reiterating the huge demand for ATP of the heart alone. Give examples of foods and how the catabolism eventually yields monosaccharides, which then enter glycolysis, etc.

    b. Lipids—Explain the body's necessity of having waterproof skin in order to maintain homeostasis. Use familiar analogies for EMS providers: fingertips getting "pruney" after prolonged exposure to water (in a bath) or after working a structure fire while wearing nonporous gloves. Refer to the typical high-fat EMS diet to make the connection between triglyceride intake and atherosclerosis.

c. Proteins—Introduce proteins in terms of insulin diabetes mellitus, a disease the average EMT knows well, although the pathophysiology may have yet to be explained in detail. Understanding that the intake of proteins provides sufficient amino acids for the production of insulin molecules gives a nice reinforcement of the earlier concept of synthesis reactions. A brief overview of protein structure will help illuminate the basic steps of protein synthesis from the amino acid building blocks. Remind the students that protein synthesis will be further studied in Chapter 3.

d. Nucleic acids/Nucleotides—Describe the basic structure of normal DNA. This will allow later reference to DNA alterations, such as UV light destruction progressing to skin melanomas. EMS workers are providing an increasing amount of emergency care to chronically ill cancer patients, so understanding the pathogenesis of these diseases will have a practical application, as well as an emotional impact on the EMS student.

e. Enzymes—Explain that enzyme function is based heavily on homeostatic norms such as temperature and pH, and that pharmacologic action is further dependent on appropriate enzyme function.

f. High-energy compounds—Describe the connection between the structure of ATP and the frequently used drug Adenocard. (This provides a good example, although the action of adenosine in arresting supraventricular tachycardias is not completely understood).

CHAPTER 3

Cell Structure and Function

INTRODUCTION

Many paramedics feel conceptually distant from microscopic structures, so that cellular structure and function becomes a particularly difficult topic to teach. The key to motivation is constantly reminding the student that a thorough understanding of cellular functioning will be the foundation of a physiologic knowledge base, particularly when the paramedic later applies this internal database to pharmacological and other treatment modalities.

After a firm grasp of normal cellular functioning is achieved, relating abnormal cellular structure and malfunction to pathologic conditions allows the paramedic to grasp the material and emotionally embrace the topic as a whole. The student now <u>cares</u> about what he or she is trying to learn, even though it is a difficult task.

LECTURE NOTES AND TEACHING STRATEGIES

1. **Fluidity of Cells**—Conceptually, one of the most important yet difficult ideas for students to grasp is the fluidity of cells. Models, diagrams, and photographs of cells all show a seemingly concrete structure, when in reality they are completely opposite in form. Pointing out to students how much they themselves move and grow just in everyday life helps explain this concept. Analogies are always helpful when discussing cellular structures and organelles:

    a. Cells—Fill balloons with gelatin and engage students in discussion about what *fluid mosaic* really means. Remind students that 80% of an average cell is water. Helpful analogies are a sink filled with water, with ice cubes or ping-pong balls floating on the surface, sides touching. Should an object be placed in the sink or removed from the water, the cubes/balls will fill in instantly and no hole will be left in the surface. The ice cubes represent the phospholipids of the cellular membrane, and as channels open or close, the phospholipids adjust, so that no membrane is lost.

b. Phospholipid bilayer—Mention that this bilayer provides the waterproofing to the cell, which exists in an aqueous environment. This is why cells do not dissolve in water.

c. Cholesterol—Compare to $2'' \times 4''$ wooden beams inside the walls of a house. This is important to note, especially with the negative attention given by popular media to cholesterol and atherosclerosis.

d. Membrane-bound proteins:

 • Receptors—Discuss the lock and key model for hormone and enzyme functioning (estrogen circulating in males, but few receptors that "fit").

 • Channels—Discuss aquaporin channel creation, with shape specificity to water molecules, under the influence of antidiuretic hormone (ADH); discuss how alcohol and caffeine function as diuretics.

 • Identifiers—Describe how identifiers give "ID badges" to cells, so that self-tissues are not attacked by immune response. Briefly discuss rheumatoid arthritis and other autoimmune disorders, where these ID markers are not recognized and thereby destroyed as "foreign."

 • Carriers—Describe the "shuttle service" for products/waste of cellular manufacture.

e. Cytosol—Review the properties of water from the previous chapter as a universal solvent with exceptionally high specific heat and pressure-resistant properties. Also reinforce prior discussions of electrolytes to encourage understanding of cytosol composition. Reiterate earlier conversations about how much cells really move and change based on alterations in the body's demands and how properties of cytosol help accomplish this goal.

2. **Selective permeability**—Review the earlier discussion about ice cubes floating on the surface of water representing structures of cellular membrane. Add the idea that these ice cubes could "choose" to allow one substance to enter but not another, based on the cells' needs.

3. **Passive vs. active processes**—The difference between these processes is based on energy requirement. A brief but critical aside that will be reinforced often in future lectures should be stated now. A very simple understanding of the Krebs/Citric Acid/TCA cycle is important for the EMS student. A constant emergency care premise of "Airway, airway, airway," when prioritizing patient treatment needs has been stressed since the EMT-Basic's first lectures, but students are not often told *why* the airway is so critical. It is helpful now to show the connection between oxygen availability and energy production, as it will clarify not only the current lecture but many future topics as well.

> *Glycolysis:* in cytosol, glucose $\rightarrow$ $\rightarrow$ pyruvate
>
> anaerobic/no oxygen required
>
> small energy gain = 2 ATP for each glucose
>
> *Kreb's/Electron Transport:*
>
> in mitochondria (organelle to be discussed later)
>
> > pyruvate $\rightarrow$ $\rightarrow$ in presence of oxygen,
> >
> > > huge energy gain = 36 ATP from each glucose
> > >
> > > compare to profit margin of average retail store
> > >
> > > without oxygen, pyruvate $\rightarrow$ $\rightarrow$ lactic acid, no ATP gain
> > >
> > > lactic acid = "no pain, no gain" of resistance training or chest
> > >
> > > > pain with myocardial infarction

Net conclusion:

Airway, Airway, Airway!

4. **Diffusion, osmosis, facilitated diffusion, and filtration**—Point out that all of these processes are passive; they require no energy. Movement is along a concentration gradient.

5. **Diffusion, osmosis**—Explain that the concentration of any solution seeks equality, with motion by both particles (diffusion) and water (osmosis). Since EMS students are well familiar with the use of IV fluids and bolus medications, they usually grasp this concept well.

6. **Facilitated diffusion**—Point out that this is the mechanism of insulin and glucose bonding, where insulin knows the "secret password" to the cellular "door" and glucose does not. EMS students easily understand this concept also since complications from diabetes are such a frequent 911 call occurrence. Remind students that only a "facilitator" is needed, but not energy, due to the concentration gradient.

7. **Filtration**—Explain that filtration is based on particle size only. A pasta strainer analogy works well here; anything small enough to flow through the holes will do so. Larger objects cannot pass.

8. **Active transport**—How the EMS instructor further tackles this important yet sometimes difficult concept depends greatly on the sequence of learning in the particular education system. If paramedic students have already been exposed to depolarization, usually in an EKG recognition course, this concept is easy for them. If not, a slower and more methodical technique must be used. Teaching tip: Use different colored chalk to show particles and water. Draw simple sketches of adjacent cells with various examples of movement across cell membranes and have students name the process correctly. Students

can take turns drawing and challenging each other.

9. **Fluid tonicity**—Draw upon the students' knowledge of IV fluid use, especially in resuscitation, when large quantities of fluid may be given. Use extreme examples of dextrose in 50% water and sterile water and have students try to anticipate how this will affect red blood cells based on membrane permeability (hypertonic, RBCs shrink; hypotonic, RBCs swell and lyse).

10. **Organelles**—Whenever possible, include clinical examples in your description of how each organelle functions. For instance, what would happen to patient if an organelle malfunctions? Examples: (a) rough endoplasmic reticulum—diabetes (inappropriate insulin production); (b) smooth endoplasmic reticulum—multiple sclerosis (inappropriate myelin synthesis).

CHAPTER 4

The Tissue Level of Organization

INTRODUCTION

For the EMS provider, a solid, basic understanding of tissue structure and function will lay the groundwork for topics critical to patient care, such as the circulatory and nervous systems. Seeing how some cancers can alter cell shape and function will provide a deeper understanding of the medical complications arising from both the disease and the treatments. Closer inspection of tissue structure and function will provide good reinforcement of the earlier, more cumbersome topics of biochemistry and the cellular aspects of life.

LECTURE NOTES AND TEACHING STRATEGIES

1. **Outline the four types of tissue and their basic functions.** The beautiful simplicity of the human body is perhaps best summed up by saying that every inherent structure fits into one of only four tissue types: epitheleal, muscle, nervous, and connective. Epithelial, muscle, and nervous tissues are clear-cut and fit neatly into their simple definitions. *Connective tissue,* however, is best thought of as a "garbage" term used to collectively describe all the structures left over when epithelial, muscle, and nervous tissues are ruled out. Also, briefly explain the germ layer origins of each tissue; this will help later with pathophysiology discussions.

2. **Describe the functions of the epithelia**. EMS students will relate well with these points as the study and treatment of soft tissue injuries comprises much of their job. Describe a motorcycle accident victim with significant "road rash" and then lead the class in an interactive discussion regarding the cell destruction, loss of cytosol, extreme pain response, and risk of infection that will probably follow, based on loss of epithelial tissue.

3. **Discuss intercellular connections.** The EMT already has a basic understanding of many body systems and their functions. Discussing gap junctions now will help to illuminate later topics, such as cardiac function and tight junctions protecting the GI tract. This also sets up further conversations about pathophysiology in future lessons.

4. **Explain the cell layers.** This is another perfect "Art 101" class activity, as students can help draw and label cell layer types, using colored chalk. Prepare three-by-five note cards; write the name of one cell layer type on each card. Then pass out the cards to the students; have them draw the appropriate cell type on the board and then challenge each other to properly name the cells.

5. **Discuss the glandular epithelium..** While the drawings of cells are still on the board, have the students visualize how specialization of these cells can encourage the manufacture of hormones and allow for their secretion. This also makes clear how the effect of the hormone will be based on how far it travels (paracrine vs. endocrine effects).

6. **Compare types of muscle tissue.** A comparative histology overhead (or slide, drawing, or other visual) will instantly reveal the critical differences among these structures. Again, the EMT enters this A&P course with a rudimentary understanding of heart function. This visual aid will build on that knowledge by showing exactly how the muscle types differ and how form follows function. For example, skeletal muscle can create forceful contractions, due to very organized structure. The "chaos" of smooth muscle does not allow for strong contraction, but it does not require constant CNS control, either. Draw a simple sarcomere and describe how the sliding filaments create contraction. Although the muscles will be covered further in future lectures, this brief introduction is a good time investment.

7.**Describe nervous tissue.** Use a simple sketch of an axon to illuminate the functional cell of this system. The concept of neurotransmitter function at the synapse is a good segue into a discussion of psychiatric pharmacology. The EMT is very familiar with the end result of this topic, both from emergency medicine (so many calls with depressed patients) and the popular press (newspaper and magazine articles describing SSRI medications at the lay person's level).

8. **Discuss connective tissue.** The epithelial, muscle, and nervous cell types have clear, precise differences. Connective tissue, on the other hand, has a broader definition, so discussing it last helps to explain that it includes all tissues in the body, without fitting into the exact definitions of the prior three. Define *connective tissue* as "specialized cells suspended in a matrix." Then begin with the most liquid matrix (blood) and progress gradually to the most solid (bone). For the most part, histology photos/drawings are not very helpful for this lesson unless time permits in-depth explanations of the histologic structures.

Special note: Based on their tendency to be active people by nature, EMS providers learn best by doing. Therefore, this lesson's emphasis on drawing, both by the instructor and the student, is critical for its absorption. When their instructor draws on the board, most students will copy the drawings into their notes. When the instructor uses prepared visuals, such as slides, overheads, or Powerpoint, students are less inclined to copy the illustrations drawings into their notes. This undermines success during their studying at home, when they either do not have sketches for reference or cannot recall specific points about the cell illustrations in the textbook.

The emphasis is not on the artistic ability of the instructor but rather on emotionally engaging the students with the material through psychomotor activity. Any time a lesson involves topics or structures that the EMT cannot visualize on a patient, further effort by the instructor, such as these aforementioned sketches, is essential for student involvement and comprehension.

CHAPTER 5

The Integumentary System

INTRODUCTION

The integumentary system's greatest impact for EMS students lies in the skin's potential to be their best assessment tool in patient care. Assessing the skin is a constant in all patient scenarios and is done without any equipment other than the EMS provider's eyes and hands. In many treatment situations, the patient's skin reveals far more than the heart monitor, blood pressure, or pulse oximetry can.

LECTURE NOTES AND TEACHING STRATEGIES

1. **Functions of the skin.** Begin with an in-depth, EMS-focused discussion regarding the functions of the skin, as they all pertain strongly to patient assessment in the prehospital setting. The initial impression of any patient begins with assessing the skin color, the very instant the EMT has eye contact with the patient's body, although this analysis may be subconscious!

   a. Protection—Differentiate the potential sequelae that will follow the loss of skin integrity in a variety of soft-tissue injuries. For example, explain that punctures pose less risk for hemorrhage but greater risk of infection, while abrasions present great risk for infection and loss of cellular and interstitial fluid but not for loss of blood. Lacerations, on the other hand, present huge risk of hemorrhage but less for infection as blood flow flushes out pathogens.

   b. Temperature regulation—Explain that burn patients transition quickly from hyperthermia to hypothermia, and discuss how to anticipate this occurrence. Also point out the skin's function as a blood reservoir. In early shock, peripheral

16

vasoconstriction encourages blood shunting to the core.

    c.   Storage of nutrients—Describe how geriatric patients lose subcutaneous adipose tissue and therefore have fewer available nutrients and inefficient temperature regulation.

    d.   Sensory reception—Explain the importance of pain relief for the injured patient. For example, the victim of a motorcycle wreck may be so distracted by the excruciating pain caused by extensive abrasions on his extremities that he (and the paramedic) may not initially notice the dyspnea and cyanosis developing from a pneumothorax also suffered in the accident.

    e.   Excretion and secretion—Discuss the diagnosis of several diseases, such as cystic fibrosis, based on the quality of the patient's sweat. Note that the body uses this pathway to excrete other wastes, as well.

2. **Anatomical structures of the skin**

    a.   Epidermis—Refer to skin conditions such as blisters, corns, and calluses while discussing the normal epidermal anatomy. This will make an emotional connection for EMS students, who typically know a lot about their own skin maladies that are due to the very physical nature of EMS. Also, discuss the importance of cultural sensitivity for the EMT to introduce your presentation about epidermal pigments; ethnic differences are perhaps only skin deep!

    b.   Dermis—Reiterate the huge amount of information that the central nervous system receives from the peripheral nerves in the dermis. These nerves flood the CNS with data regarding significant injuries, further altering everything from the patients' mental status to vital signs. Emphasize again the huge amount of blood flow to the dermis and how transient this flow can be, either in shunting or in the extremes of hypothermia and hyperthermia.

c. Sebaceous glands—Point out the sebaceous glands' importance to EMS providers' own well-being. Intact skin is the body's best defense against pathogenic infection, and sebum is an important natural emollient to promote the skin's integrity. However, few professions are as hard on the skin as EMS. Have the students examine their own hands, with all their scrapes, scratches, and other injuries. Mention that the frequency with which all medical professionals must wash their hands exacerbates this constant integumentary assault. Remind students to apply lotion or other emollients (functioning as artificial sebum) every time they wash their hands.

d. Sweat glands—Discuss the various factors that can alter the sweating mechanism (medicinal and illicit drugs, psychiatric disorders, thyroid malfunction) and the severe conditions that develop. Illustrate the body's cooling mechanisms in addition to evaporation (conduction, convection, radiation). Pay particular attention to the especially altered systems of the very young and very old, since these age groups make up a large portion of EMS patients.

e. Subcutaneous adipose tissue—Discuss in detail transdermal medication administration, noting that its use is becoming more and more widespread. A good connection for EMS providers is to consider why the "patch" is excellent for the geriatric patient but can be limited by both the decline of the patient's body and the patient's living conditions. Adipose tissues decrease due to the body's need for the stored fuel, and with decreased lipids under the skin, absorption also decreases. Advanced arteriosclerosis and atherosclerosis to dermal capillaries decrease circulation to transport absorbed medication. Living on a decreased income may mean too-cold houses in the winter and too-warm in the summer. Medication administration from the patch is based on normal body temperature, so in these extremes medications may be absorbed either too slowly or too quickly.

Use the following scenario to illuminate this point: A 74-year-old male who lives in a 50°F apartment in winter slips on icy steps. He is placed in a warm ambulance for transport due to the injury. His blood pressure begins to fall drastically. Why? (His nitroglycerin patch suddenly overmedicates him, as the medication is overabsorbed in the warmer environment, causing greater systemic vasodilation than expected.

    f. Injury and repair—Reiterate definitions and diagnosis of burn types and critical burn areas, as well as ways to measure the affected area. Explain the "rule of nines" and the "rule of one." Remind students of proper assessment, dressing, and further treatment. Explain why the partial-thickness burn has blisters, why the full-thickness burn shows no pain, and why all burn patients are at risk for hypothermia, hypoperfusion, and infection. The stronger the EMS providers' physiologic knowledge base, the better suited they are to anticipate a patient's potential turn for the worse.

3. Conclusion Lead a class discussion regarding various skin colorations and their pathophysiological meaning. Ask students to name various skin color changes and then briefly describe their possible causes. For instance, cyanosis results from decreased oxygen presence on hemoglobin, altering pigment shape and light reflection, while pallor results from vasoconstriction of dermal capillaries. Thus, cyanosis indicates a decrease in blood *quality*, while pallor indicates a decrease in blood *quantity*. What if the patient has both? Cyanosis and pallor together result in ashen skin. Treatments for these two conditions are not necessarily the same.

Finally as an EMS-related aside, note the benefits and drawbacks of pulse oximetry. When this approximation of oxygen saturation became part of the EMS standard of care, too much faith could be placed on its readings. This is a good time to point out that many variables can alter the pulse oximeter's efficiency. For example, carbon monoxide levels in a smoker's blood stream are higher than normal. As this alters hemoglobin functioning, it also alters its shape and therefore its color, possibly causing a false-high pulse oximetry reading. In turn, this data may lead the paramedic to misinterpret the patient's respiratory status. Remind your students that patient assessment is about the patient and not about our technological toys.

CHAPTER 6

The Skeletal System

INTRODUCTION

The most important thing for the EMS provider to learn from a lesson on the skeletal system is that while few patients die acutely from fractures, the original trauma and resulting pain and discomfort can drastically affect the patient, both emotionally and physiologically. The average EMT tends to think of a fracture as a relatively minor call, but the patient's short- and long-term homeostasis can be significantly altered by the fracture. Luckily the vast majority of fractures do not lead to life-threatening complications, but the potential still exists and therefore must be anticipated and carefully monitored by the EMT.

LECTURE NOTES AND TEACHING STRATEGIES

1. **Bone functions:**

   a. Support/protection—Explain that the EMT must constantly assume the worst about all injuries. If a bone is damaged, the EMT must assume that the underlying tissue is equally disrupted. Since the role of bone is to provide protection throughout the body, the loss of a bone's integrity can be disastrous for the rest of the body.

   b. Storage—Briefly describe calcium metabolism and homeostatic control. (This will be discussed further in the gastrointestinal and endocrine lectures, but it is important for students to begin to imagine all the control factors in place to keep blood calcium levels within very narrow limits. A good example is to imagine a student (I usually choose a young, strapping male with a good sense of humor!) consuming a box of cookies and an entire half-gallon of milk after a particularly draining day on the ambulance. Since the student will not necessarily suffer a kidney stone, the surge of calcium into his blood stream must have activated some homeostatic controls. (This is a good opportunity to reinforce negative feedback concepts.) The student does not have to consume any more calcium for a week, yet his body will continue to monitor and control both his blood and bone calcium levels.

   c. Marrow protection—Describe the location and function of marrow within the medullary cavities. Explain the concept of yellow (quiescent) and red (active) marrow and the transition from one to the other as it pertains to post-trauma care, especially in the case of multiple bone fractures with blood loss and the risk of pulmonary embolism. The formed elements and their multiple functions will be discussed in later chapters, but the marrow's location within the bony spaces is important for the paramedic to know.

2. **Generic long bone**—Draw and label a long bone, and encourage students to draw their own renditions.

   a. Compact vs spongy bone—Explain why impact to bones at different points can cause different injuries. (This is a good opportunity to reinforce mechanism of injury concepts.) Discuss how differences among bone types relate to the functions of muscle attachment, motion, and range of motion and to the bone's potential for damage?

   b. Medullary cavity—Describe the locations of red vs yellow marrow in the body and explain the difference.

   c. Periosteum—Explain how a severely fractured bone can result in a nondisplaced fracture, as long as the periosteum remains intact. This is a vivid reminder of how a poorly applied splint can cause a nondisplaced fracture to become a displaced one.

   d. Articular cartilage—Discuss how the depth of cartilage will vary based on the needs of the joint. Explain that the articular cartilage is the point of attack in the autoimmune malfunction of rheumatoid arthritis.

    e. Perforating canals—Explain why the injury of large bones can result in huge blood loss and why intraosseous infusions work so well. (Depending on time constraints and where students are in their advanced life support coursework, use this as the starting point for an in-depth discussion of the technique and methodology of intraosseous infusions.)

3. Bone development and growth

    a. Osteoclast/osteoblast function—Discuss how the osteoblasts' and osteoclasts' actions must be balanced to maintain bone integrity. Describe alterations during puberty, osteoporosis, and Paget's disease.

    b. Epiphyseal growth plates—Explain why treating the pediatric patient with an extremity injury is especially critical due to the fragile nature of growth centers. This point offers a good opportunity to reinforce splinting rules and techniques. A good splint may preserve growth plate function, while a poor splint may irreversibly disrupt growth plate function, causing significant disfigurement.

4. Injury and repair

    a. Discuss the potential complications to the post-trauma patient. Offer as an example the post-femur-fracture patient who now calls 911 because of severe dyspnea. Explain where the blood clot that caused the pulmonary embolus came from, how the dyspnea was created, and discuss what could have prevented this problem.

    b. Explain how EMS providers can anticipate child or geriatric abuse by assessing for partially healed old fractures or multiple injuries in different stages of healing.

5. Overview of the skeleton/classification of fractures—Use a fully-articulated skeleton model (life-size, preferably) as a basis for class discussion. This exercise can elicit excellent student participation.

Start at the head, encouraging students to name all the bones that they know, always using the correct medical terminology. Reinforce the importance for paramedics to use appropriate location terminology in their role as the "eyes, ears, and hands of the OMD." *Example:* "The injury is three inches distal to the elbow, on the lateral side of the radius."

With each bone, discuss mechanisms of injury and which type of fracture is likely, also adding worst-case scenario complications and treatment options. *Example:* Injury—clavicle fracture from falling on outstretched arm, causing transverse or spiral fracture, lacerating subclavian vein, causing severe hypovolemia or puncturing lung, causing pneumothorax. Best treatment—sling and swath for the arm. Conclusion—simply naming bones might become boring, but imagining multiply injured patients, how they were injured, and how to treat them is fascinating.

As you move inferiorly on the skeleton, include articulations in your discussion, along with their definitions and expected range of motion. Discuss potential complications with dislocations of each joint, such as nerve and vessel entrapment at the elbow and ankle.

6. **Conclusion**—Conclude the lesson discussing special considerations of the age-extreme patient. You have already mentioned disrupted growth plates in the pediatric patient and osteoporosis in the geriatric patient; now point out a few pertinent points about assessing these special patients.

   a. The pediatric patient is more difficult to assess for fractures. This is partially due to greenstick fractures and the absence of the expected signs of injury (edema, ecchymosis, and deformity). In addition, a huge fear factor coupled with a lessened ability to communicate and express emotions makes the assessment, treatment, packaging, and transport of a pediatric patient particularly difficult. More than ever, the paramedic must use excellent communication skills and gentle mannerisms in treating this patient, while remaining constantly vigilant to potential complications. Always assume the worst injury—no reasonable parents will ever blame a paramedic for overtreating their child.

b. The geriatric patient can have greater complications from a simple fracture. Due to chronic medical conditions, an initially uncomplicated hip fracture may lead to a myocardial infarction or stroke in the geriatric patient. The resulting pain alone may dangerously exacerbate chronic dysrhythmias or hypertension. Due to insufficient nutritional intake, a bone injury may heal poorly, causing deformity and poor mobility and increasing the likelihood that the patient will fall again, causing further damage throughout the body.

CHAPTER 7

The Muscular System

INTRODUCTION

The muscular system represents a major portion of the body; therefore, its functioning plays a large role in homeostasis. The EMS provider must have a very detailed understanding of cardiac muscle, in particular. Cardiac muscle will be covered in depth in later chapters, but a basic understanding of all muscle types is important to overall patient care. While injuries solely to the muscular structures will not kill a patient immediately, the EMT needs to anticipate possible complications from these injuries, understand how to prevent them, and know the potential short- and long-term effects of abnormal muscle functioning.

Note: Depending on time constraints some of this information may have been covered already during the lecture on Chapter 4, The Tissue Level of Organization. Assess how much needs to be repeated for clarity or depth of understanding. Also, muscle and skeletal systems can be taught together since many concepts of patient care regarding these systems overlap. Many instructors will find it helpful to divert in-depth cardiac and smooth muscle information to the circulatory and digestive system lectures and to cover only the basic cellular differences among the muscle types here.

LECTURE NOTES AND TEACHING STRATEGIES

1. **Muscle cells**—Lead a group activity naming the four characteristics of muscle cells (elasticity, excitability, extensibility, and contractility). This brain-storming session will help students orient themselves to muscle functioning.

2. **Muscle functions**—Lead a class discussion on the relevance of muscle functions to emergency care. Most functions will be obvious to the students, but their particular EMS

implications need to be addressed. *Example:* In maintaining body temperature, two-thirds of energy expended during contraction creates heat, one-third creates work or movement. Therefore, the immobilized trauma patient has increased potential to become hypothermic, as the heat source is restricted. Age-extreme patients have lesser ability still to create enough body heat from muscle contraction.

3. **Cellular structure**—Draw a sequential diagram showing an entire muscle, beginning with the individual sarcomeres, to help students picture how functional units cumulatively create the function of entire muscle. Draw a simple sarcomere on the far left side of board and then sequentially depict how the stimulus to contract alters sarcomere anatomy. If the concept of neurons was covered in earlier lectures, then the addition of the nerve stimulus to these drawings is a logical development. Projecting a well-drawn diagram of the entire structure, including sarcoplasmic reticulum and t-tubules, on the overhead while drawing the simple sketches on the board can be helpful. This allows for constant reinforcement of how the impulse can continue into deeper myofibrils. Give contrasting examples of nerve/cell ratios (1:5 for finger tip, 1:100 for back muscles) to illuminate how fine motor control is achieved. Having these diagrams present also helps to explain the counterintuitive concept of the "All or None Principle" and how altering muscle recruitment at the CNS results in varying muscular action.

Reinforce the concept of glycolysis and Kreb's cycle and the critical need for available oxygen in your discussion of the cell's dependence on energy for functioning. The EMT can never be reminded enough how important good airway status is for patient homeostasis. Also, since most EMS providers do some type of regular exercise, they are familiar with the "burn" of lactic acid during a workout. Explaining more critical muscles, such as the heart or diaphragm, in these terms puts an important spin on the concept of "no pain, no gain."

4. **Naming of muscles**—Identify and discuss muscle groups, using the model skeleton. Group muscles as flexors, extensors, and so forth, to help illuminate their actions and potential complications to their injuries. *Example:* If the quadriceps muscles are in spasm following an injury during a high-school football game, what damage might these muscles be doing to the patella and underlying structures? What can the EMT do to alleviate this?

    Note: An understanding of muscle groups and their relevance to prehospital care is a much more important educational objective for the EMS provider than is an encyclopedic knowledge of muscle identification.

5. **Conclusion**—Emphasize the importance of assuming the worst about all muscular injuries. When any part of the body is injured, the EMT must assume that all underlying tissues are maximally injured and treat the patient accordingly.

CHAPTER 8

Neural Tissue and the Central Nervous System

INTRODUCTION

The importance to the EMS provider of learning the nervous system well is basic: to understand any machine, you must first understand how it is controlled. When normal control and function are your well-understood baseline, anticipating and dealing with abnormal functioning is much easier. (Note: Cranial and spinal nerves can either be discussed now or with Chapter 9.)

LECTURE NOTES AND TEACHING STRATEGIES

1. **Nervous system overview**

   a. Central nervous system—brain, spinal cord

   b. Peripheral nervous system—12 pairs cranial nerves, 31 pairs spinal nerves

      (1)   Sensory (afferent)

      (2)   Motor (efferent)

         (a)   Somatic (conscious control)

         (b)   Autonomic (unconscious control)

            i.   Parasympathetic ("feed and breed")

            ii. Sympathetic ("fight or flight")

2. **Cranial nerves**—Emphasize that the cranial nerves belong to the peripheral nervous system even though they are located within the cranium; show a diagram explaining how they are numbered in order from anterior to posterior. This helps students memorize their functions. Models or actual human brains help illustrate this point dramatically.

3. **Spinal nerves**—Show a diagram of dermatomes.

a. Discuss acute spinal injured patients and how a dermatome is easily assessed in the acutely injured patient (skin can be dramatically different in sensation, color, temperature, and quality above and below the level of spinal injury).

b. Also emphasize that spinal deficits can often be reversed with time, reduction of spinal edema, the use of corticosteroids, or other treatments, so the paramedic should try not to let these findings alarm the patient. These patients are often already very fearful, so calm reassurance by the EMS professional is critical for the patient's emotional welfare.

4. **Motor nerves vs. sensory nerves**—Explain that these are two different nerves, so paramedics must assess both functions during all patient encounters, particularly when the mechanism of injury indicates spinal damage or extremity injuries.

5. **Sympathetic nervous system vs. parasympathetic nervous system**—Emphasize that the parasympathetic nervous system is almost always in control. Students will have good examples to understand the sympathetic response, both from their own response after a "good" call (hyperactive, attention to detail) and from patients in hypoperfusion shock. These are dramatic examples of sympathetic effects, but make it clear that the system functions consistently to help maintain blood pressure (sleep vs. awake), and other physiologic functions.

6. **Micro-anatomic structures:**

a. Neurons—discuss the natural cell death rate (~250,000/day) in an average adult, and explain how stress, poor nutrition, chronic fatigue, drugs, alcohol, or other problems can greatly increase cell death rates. A colorful discussion usually ensues, showing that these characteristics are common in EMS and how our profession/lifestyle is hard on the CNS.

b. Synapse—Describe the huge focus of the pharmaceutical industry on the synapses.

Discuss the explosion in the use of selective serotonin reuptake inhibitors (SSRI), how they work at the synapse, and their impact on patient behavior.

c. Myelin—Explain the importance of lipid intake in diet. Describe the many disorders related to myelin malfunction (multiple sclerosis, Guillain-Barre syndrome, Tay-Sachs syndrome), and discuss myelin's importance to axon regeneration (the greater stimulus when myelin sheath fragments are still present).

d. Neuroglia—since neurons do not divide after early childhood, it is the alteration of DNA and further mutation in these cells that leads to brain tumors. Specific glial cells to mention: astrocytes, which create the blood-brain barrier (important to use of medications by paramedics); and ependymal cells, which produce cerebrospinal fluid).

7. **Membrane Potential:**

a. Repeat the airway/ATP emphasis from Chapter 3, while discussing the need of energy for active transport. Discuss the threshold, and use the electrical chaos of seizures to illustrate what happens when thresholds are reached and cells are stimulated during partial repolarization. Coordinate this discussion with ventricular fibrillation (even EMT-Basics should have basic understanding of this, based on their knowledge about automatic external defibrillators).

b. Emphasize that reflex arcs should NOT be tested in EMS because of the potential exacerbation of traumatic injuries during muscular response. While some spinal injuries may dampen reflexive responses, others can enhance those responses.

8. **Gross anatomy:**

a. Dura mater—Note that the dura mater is identical to pericardial sac, both in function and structure. Explain that when hemorrhage exists under the dura, blood tends to be held in a specific spot due to the inelasticity of dura, so a nervous system deficit will tend to be more focal. For example, a subdural bleed in an area of the left cerebellum may affect only balance, coordination, and muscle function of the right side of body.

Discuss coup vs. contracoup injuries, and explain that the paramedic cannot necessarily tell where an injury is within the cranium based on the site of the impact to the head. For instance, the patient's head strikes a windshield, but the worst injury may be at the occiput due to contracoup forces. Warn students to be prepared for unusual presentations during development of intracranial pressure. Describe the "lucid interval" and explain why students should not be lulled into a false sense of security regarding the patient's condition.

b. Arachnoid: Explain that the arachnoid has a loose tissue structure, so bleeds may be more extensive. They can be spontaneous, due to congenital defects, which may give unusual and therefore unanticipated patient presentations (for example, the 25-year-old female with a recent history of severe headache today becomes syncopal during aerobics class and presents with respiratory arrest during transport: expect the worst, and therefore be more prepared.)

c. Cerebrospinal fluid—Explain that if cerebrospinal fluid is leaking from the cranium (via the nose, mouth, or ears) then there MUST be a fracture/hole somewhere in the system, since the fluid is contained in a closed system. Getting verification of cerebrospinal fluid's presence in the blood ("halo test") is a helpful, but emphasize that doing so should NEVER take extra time and effort during a call on such a critical patient. Also, point out that the system that both produces new CSF and resorbs old CSF can be damaged by trauma, so post-closed-head-injury patients may have hydrocephalic complications requiring shunts or other treatments. In the growing field of critical care transport, paramedics are likely to encounter this type of patient.

d. Pia mater—Compare the pia mater to plastic wrap covering the surface of a bowl of oatmeal: it does not provide much protection, but it holds everything together as a unit, covering the multitudes of folds, otherwise known as sulci and gyri.

e. Cerebrum—Point out that the affected area may show strange and unanticipated personality variants (for instance, the frontal lobe = inappropriate sexual behavior; the temporal lobe = inability to store new information, so the patient asks repeatedly what happened previously). This can be very frustrating and frightening to the patient and very annoying to the paramedic. In such instances, the paramedic can write a short version of the MVA and give it to the patient to read and reread.)

Dysphasias caused by injuries to speech and/or memory centers can also be very disturbing to patients, as the words they form in their minds are not the words that come out of their mouths. Warn students to be prepared for frightened and panicked patients—their emotional concerns are as important as their physical injuries. Stress the need for frequent reassessments, and reassurances, of head-injured patients.

f. Corpus callosum—Explain the corpus callosum's involvement in seizure disorders as it enhances and increases electrical chaos between hemispheres. For example, a focal seizure seen in one extremity then spreads into full tonic clonic activity involving the entire body.

g. Circle of Willis/CNS blood supply—Emphasize the brain's huge need for blood. It weighs about 3 pounds in an average adult but requires 20 percent of cardiac output. It utilizes only glucose and huge amounts of oxygen since it cannot store fuel for future use. The brain is the only tissue in the body that can utilize glucose without insulin.

h. Hypothalamus—Explain that the hypothalamus is responsible for so many functions that many disorders can originate here, including diabetes insipidus, premature labor, abnormal pH, temperature and water regulation disorders, and hypothyroidism.

i. Pons—Explain that the pons assists with breathing rhythmicity and thus is the site for Cheyne-Stokes respirations. Point out that Cheyne Stokes respirations do not necessarily mean the patient is profoundly affected; they may be normal for patients at high elevations or in the very young and very old. But stress that paramedics should assume that Cheyne Stokes respirations are a pathological sign until proven otherwise. Discuss the importance of using positive-pressure ventilation to control respirations, thus overriding abnormal respiratory patterns.

j. Medulla oblongata—Explain that the medulla oblongata is most critical to the maintenance of homeostasis. It is the site of the vasomotor center, respiratory drive, and cardiac center, so damage to the medulla is immediately life-threatening. Show a cranium model or a picture of a foramen magnum to illustrate how and why increased pressure to the medulla during herniation syndrome causes Cushing's triad (hypertension with widened pulse pressure, bradycardia, and respiratory abnormalities).

9. **Aging**—Explain that post-CVA patients must relearn functions (talking, walking, memory) because the brain does not "heal." Alzheimer's patients can be very challenging to manage due to personality changes and widely varying health problems. They can be combative, childlike, and uncommunicative. This condition also is very difficult for care providers, both emotionally and physically, so the EMT must assess them to make sure they are not "patients" too.

CHAPTER 9

The Peripheral Nervous System and Integrated Neural Functions

INTRODUCTION

While the central nervous system functions as a control center for the body, the peripheral nervous system is the critical conduit of this information to the rest of the body. The five-star general is only as effective as the lowly soldier who carries out his commands.

Note: The central and peripheral nervous systems can be taught as separate units or as a single unit. Several points from Chapter I are repeated here for that purpose. Cranial and spinal nerves can be discussed either now or with Chapter 8.

LECTURE NOTES AND TEACHING STRATEGIES

1. **Cranial nerves**—Emphasize that the cranial nerves belong to the peripheral nervous system even though they are located within the cranium. Show a diagram explaining how they are numbered in order from anterior to posterior. This helps students memorize their functions. Models or actual human brains help illustrate this point dramatically. Also have on hand a skull model to demonstrate the passageway of nerves out of the foramen magnum and other characteristics of the cranial vault.

   a. Class participation activity: try to invent new/fun mnemonic devices to remember nerve order and function. (For example: Oh Once One Takes The Anatomy Final, Very Good Vacations Are Heavenly.) Encourage creativity in making up new sayings.

   b Special note about the oculomotor nerve (III): Many EMS providers are under the initial impression that the oculomotor nerve is more sensitive to increased intracranial pressure than the other cranial nerves, since its assessment (pupils) is so greatly emphasized in EMS education. The oculomotor nerve is not actually more sensitive to pathologic pressure, but it is unique in that it allows for assessment on an unconscious, unresponsive patient, who is fully spinal-immobilized. Subtle changes in pupil size and function can help care providers anticipate a decompensating head injury, allowing them to prepare for more aggressive patient management such as hyperventilation should medullary herniation develop, endotracheal intubation, the use of mannitol or other medications to reduce cerebral edema, or the administration of corticosteroids.

2. **Spinal nerves**—Show a diagram of dermatomes.

   a. Discuss acute spinal injured patients and how a dermatome is easily assessed (skin can be dramatically different in sensation, color, temperature, and quality above and below the level of spinal injury).

   b. Also emphasize that spinal deficits can often be reversed with time, reduction of spinal edema, the use of corticosteroids, or other treatments, so the paramedic should try not to let these findings alarm the patient. These patients are often already very fearful, so calm reassurance by the EMS professional is critical for the patient's emotional welfare.

3. **Motor nerves vs. sensory nerves**—Explain that these are two different nerves, so paramedics must assess both functions during all patient encounters, particularly when the mechanism of injury indicates spinal damage or extremity injuries.

4. **Reflex arcs**—Emphasize that reflex arcs should NOT be tested in EMS because of the potential exacerbation of traumatic injuries during muscular response. Care must also be taken when assessing for sensory/pain response on injured extremities due to this reflex.

5. **Extrapyramidal reactions**—Explain the possibility of extrapyramidal reactions following ingestion of antipsychotic or antiemetic medications. These dystonias can be

seen as muscle twitching, abnormal reflex response, drooling, head or eye deviations, difficulty speaking due to abnormal tongue functioning, or abnormal gait ("Thorazine shuffle"). Intravenous diphenhydramine can lessen or reverse many of these reactions.

5. **Sympathetic nervous system vs. parasympathetic nervous system**—Emphasize that the parasympathetic nervous system is almost always in control. Students will have good examples to understand the sympathetic response, both from their own response after a "good" call (hyperactive, attention to detail) and from patients in hypoperfusion shock. These are dramatic examples of sympathetic effects, but make it clear that the system functions consistently to help maintain blood pressure (sleep vs. awake), and other physiologic functions.

   Discuss the paramedic's need to be very familiar with the two autonomic divisions since much of cardiovascular pharmacology is based on medications that either enhance or depress the sympathetic and parasympathetic functions.

6. **Class participation activity**—Go around the room and have each student name a sign of shock and explain why the patient presents this way. For example, compensated shock gives hypertension because vasoconstriction occurs. Vasoconstriction results from the release of norepinephrine due to sympathetic stimulation of the adrenal medulla. An in depth discussion on shock is the best way to lecture to EMS professionals about the sympathetic system because it both illustrates the body's response and emphasizes critical points for patient care.

CHAPTER 10

Sensory Function

INTRODUCTION

The human being is largely motivated by an urge to survive. The risk and need is based on sensory input to the brain. We are driven to see, hear, and feel much of what is around us. When these sensory functions are disrupted by illness or injury, few conditions cause more fear or anxiety. Consequently, the EMS patient who has suffered damage to these functions can be difficult to manage, and the call will be highly emotional for both the patient and the provider.

LECTURE NOTES AND TEACHING STRATEGIES

1. **Pain**—Explain that few medical care providers deal with patients in acute pain as intimately as EMS workers. They see fully the physiologic effect severe pain can elicit in their patients: their blood pressure rises, their breaths can be gasping or far too shallow, their heart races, their level of consciousness alters, and they can focus on nothing else. Discuss how the difficulty of gathering a simple patient history becomes a difficult task until the pain is controlled.

    Discuss the EMS provider's need to maintain a fine balance between alleviating the patient's discomfort and expediting transport of the patient to the care facility. This is sometimes an impossibility, as when moving the patient exacerbates the pain of an extremity fracture. Pain control can be as simple as a good splint or elevating the head of the cot or as complex as administering narcotic medications for analgesia.

2. **Baroreception**—Discuss how the complex control of perfusion based on the baroreceptors can be altered by rapid infusion of isotonic solutions, and point out that the paramedic needs to anticipate this reflex, should it occur in a deleterious manner. The

baroreceptors can also be stimulated externally; purposefully by carotid sinus massage, or accidentally by an improperly placed cervical collar.

3. **Chemoreception**—Describe how chemoreceptors are primarily responsible for control of pH and give critical input to the respiratory control. Explain that EMS providers need to understand that a wide variety of medical conditions can alter the body's normal response to these factors. Namely, both chronic and acute respiratory alterations, such as asthma or toxic inhalation, can alter the chemoreceptor mechanism, yielding inappropriate control by the CNS. Kidney and cerebral conditions can negatively affect it as well.

4. **Vision**—Explain that being an acutely optical animal, the human being relies strongly on visual information. The impact this has on patients with eye injuries is profound. The EMT must always keep in mind that an eye-injured patient is likely to be a terrified patient, regardless of mechanism of injury, age, underlying health, or any other factor.

   Emphasize that the best possible care-giving rapport and a calming demeanor are critical to this type of call. Patients should never be told they will lose an eye, or vision, or any portion of their visual acuity, regardless of their injury's presentation. Stress that it is critical to the prognosis of the injury to bandage *both* eyes, regardless of the patient's wishes.

5. **Hearing and Equilibrium**—Describe how an efficient spinal immobilization job can block the auditory canals of the ears, thus rendering the patient unable to hear clearly. The patient is already frightened and uncomfortable, strapped and taped to a rigid board, so not being able to hear becomes a major issue. Advise students not to misinterpret this agitation as an altered level of consciousness but rather to work more diligently at patient communication.

   Explain that if the inner ear is injured, the sense of equilibrium may be altered. The subsequent vertigo may elicit nausea and vomiting in the patient. This coupled with the patient's supine position immobilized on a backboard may make managing the airway a difficult but especially high priority.

6. **Age extreme patients**—Point out that age-extreme patients are particularly sensitive to the emotions of fear and uncertainty in visual and auditory difficulties, especially in the setting of an EMS call. Couple these emotions with acute pain, and this is now a very challenging call. The EMT's keeping a calm demeanor and caring communication while still maintaining professionalism is the key to handling this difficult situation.

An educational (and entertaining) activity is to have students perform a simple skill, such as applying a KED, while wearing swim goggles coated in Vaseline and earplugs, to gain a stronger sense of compassion for the geriatric patient with sensory deficits.

CHAPTER 11

The Endocrine System

INTRODUCTION

The Endocrine system is one of the hardest topics for the students to embrace, yet it becomes one of the most critical topics for them to understand once they begin to function as advanced life support providers. The efficacy of any medication depends on how well the endocrine system is functioning, and many medical conditions, both acute and chronic, either cause or exacerbate endocrine malfunction.

LECTURE NOTES AND TEACHING STRATEGIES

1. **Endocrine system overview**

   a. Provide an overview of the endocrine system. As it becomes apparent that the target organs of hormones are often distant from the original gland, explain that the key to proper hormone function is the ability for the vascular system to deliver each hormone to its appropriate target. Emphasize that this shows again how critical it is to support homeostatic perfusion in patient care. Point out the many facsimile hormones currently being synthesized and administered as medications, as each gland is discussed.

   b. Define and give examples of hormones having autocrine, paracrine, and endocrine functions. Note that not all hormone action is at distant sites. Give definitions and examples of substances as both hormones and neurotransmitters and explain why these naturally-occurring chemicals are often critical in emergency patient care settings.

   c. Describe hormone structures (amino acid derivatives, peptide, and steroid structures). This helps reinforce earlier cellular topics, such as presence of rough and smooth endoplasmic reticulum organelles and structure and function of glandular epithelium. Such reinforcement from previous lectures helps to answer the constant query of this course: "Why does a paramedic need to know or care about this?"

    d. Discuss first and second messenger systems. Use the fact that the hormone's arrival at a cell starts a chain reaction to illustrate how very many points of potential error exist in the endocrine system. Explain the concept of negative feedback to show how compensation for these potential errors might occur. Also explain how negative feedback provides the precise control required for homeostasis.

2. **Specific endocrine structures**—Discuss specific endocrine structures in terms of maladies caused by their abnormal secretion. When paramedic students can imagine dealing with a patient with each potential disorder, they emotionally embrace the topic more fully and therefore more easily absorb the cognitive information.

    a. Hypothalamus: Discuss the following points.

- The hypothalamus is the only point where endocrine and CNS interrelate, allowing for necessary redundancy between autonomic and endocrine control. The endocrine system is largely self-mediated.

- Explain that the hypothalamus is the source of hypochondriacal "diseases."

- The hypothalamus once was believed only to be the control center of the endocrine system, but now it is known to secrete hormones as well.

- Define regulatory ("tropic"), releasing, and inhibitory hormones to illustrate how precise control can be created.

    b. Pituitary gland: Explain that the anterior and posterior pituitary gland segments are completely separate in structure, secretions, and control mechanisms.

- Anterior pituitary: Discuss the following hormones.

  — Thyroid stimulating hormone is the control mechanism for the thyroid gland. Hyposecretion is not conducive to life; hypersecretion of TSH may be a compensatory mechanism caused by hyposecretion.

  — Adrenocorticotropic hormone controls glucose metabolism. (Hyposecretions and hypersecretions will be discussed later.)

  — Follicle-stimulating hormone: hyposecretion will cause inappropriate ova development in females and sperm development in males, both leading to infertility. Hypersecretion may induce multifetus pregnancies in females; it has no ill-effect in males.

  — Luteinizing hormone: hyposecretion may induce spontaneous abortions in females, as the corpus luteum is not stimulated to provide adequate progesterone early in pregnancy. Hyposecretion may cause feminization in males, as inadequate testosterone is produced by the testes. Hypersecretion in females may incite ovarian cyst formation. Hypersecretion in males may promote precocious puberty and premature closure of skeletal growth plates.

  — Prolactin: hyposecretion will cause insufficient milk production in the nursing mother. Hypersecretion may cause overproduction of milk transiently for the nursing mother, but the body will resorb any milk not consumed by her infant. Abnormal secretion has no known sequelae for the male.

— Growth hormone: hyposecretion in childhood causes *dwarfism*, while hypersecretion in childhood causes *giantism* in both sexes. Hyposecretion after puberty will give abnormal metabolism of nutrients and poor healing after injury. Hypersecretion after puberty causes *acromegaly*. Some body tissues still respond to growth stimulus after bone closure, hence the instantly recognizable abnormal facial and hand structures. In both giantism and acromegaly, it is important to note that overstimulation by growth hormone is detrimental to structures other than musculoskeletal, making these patients prone to premature cardiovascular disease development. (Note: there are many photographs of patients with these conditions; a picture is worth a thousand words!)

— Melanocyte-stimulating hormone (MSH): the full effects of MSH are not well understood. Hyposecretion and hypersecretion may alter pigmentation of the skin, but the effects of this hormone are expected to be more widespread.

Special note about the anterior pituitary: Discuss *Sheehan's syndrome* to illustrate an important point about what happens to our patients after our emergency care. Due to the anterior pituitary's important role during pregnancy and parturition, its perfusion requirements are larger than normal, so that a significant period of hypoperfusion can drastically alter its functioning. Sheehan's syndrome is a condition caused by a severe postpartum hemorrhage, which can lead to hypoglycemia, dehydration, weakness, and amenorrhea. While the recognition of this syndrome is often not found until several months following delivery and rarely involves activation of the 911/emergency care system, the severe hemorrhage during emergency childbirth quite possibly did involve EMS. This condition illustrates an important point to the paramedic about the potential development of complications in our patients following emergency care.

- Posterior pituitary: Discuss the following hormones.

    — Antidiuretic hormone is critical for maintenance of adequate blood pressure. It is inhibited by both alcohol and caffeine, albeit by different means. Discuss the new use of synthetic ADH, otherwise known as vasopressin, in cases of hypotension caused by cardiac failure or shock. Explain *diabetes insipidus,* caused either by inadequate secretion of ADH or by the kidneys' inability to react to the presence of ADH. Should a patient have this disease, the paramedic needs to expect that supporting perfusion may be more difficult than normal.

    — Oxytocin: hypersecretion in women may lead to premature labor during pregnancy or premature release of milk during lactation. Hyposecretion will inhibit normal parturition and milk release by the mammary glands. Abnormal secretion will affect emission and ejaculation in the male. The drug Pitocin is the synthetic form of this hormone, used to induce or enhance labor progression.

c. Thyroid gland: Discuss the following points about thyroid hormones (T3 and T4).

    — Hyposecretion can cause *cretinism* in childhood, presenting in severe physical and mental retardation. Supplemental thyroid hormone can halt the damage if caught early. In adulthood, hyposecretion of thyroid hormone can cause *myxedema*, with patients exhibiting lethargy, weight gain, peripheral edema, poor hair growth, and slow healing. Ever-worsening hyposecretion may be caused by an autoimmune disorder, *Hashimoto thyroiditis,* where the body continually attacks the follicular structures of the gland. Since iodine is a critical component of both thyroid hormones, a diet insufficient in iodine intake can cause a *goiter* formation. While this complication is unusual in the United States (thanks to iodized salt), goiters can be large enough to obstruct the trachea and larynx and require emergency treatment.

— Hypersecretion of T3 and T4 is called *Grave's disease* and is marked by hyperactivity, high metabolic rate causing inability to gain weight, hypertension, and exophthalmos (bulging eyeballs). Untreated, this condition can lead to increased risk of hypertensive crisis, paroxysmal supraventricular tachycardia, and myocardial infarction. Hypersecretion of thyroid hormones also promotes osteoporosis.

— Altered secretion of calcitonin rarely causes problems for patients. However, injections of the synthetic version of this hormone can be used to increase bone mass in osteoporotic patients.

d. Parathyroid glands parathyroid hormone (PTH): Explain the ability of PTH to increase calcium levels in the blood and how abnormal PTH secretion can greatly affect muscle function, specifically the myocardium, thus inducing dysrhythmias. Explain that hypocalcemia also causes muscle cramps and tetany, while hypercalcemia can promote kidney stone formation. Acid-base abnormalities make calcium balance even more difficult to obtain. Discuss the administration of magnesium sulfate in ventricular dysrhythmias to help normalize calcium levels by enhancing PTH action, therefore encouraging appropriate muscle cell function.

e. Thymus gland: Discuss the role of thymosin hormones. Essentially atrophied in the adult, the thymus has little function. Its involvement with T cell function, however, is being actively studied, due to the impact of HIV on T cells.

f. Adrenal gland: explain the functions of the adrenal cortex and the adrenal medulla.

- Adrenal cortex.

  — Describe the role of hyposecretion of corticosteroids in *Addison's disease*. Patients with this history can be especially challenging to the paramedic, due to their inherent tendency towards hypoglycemia and dehydration. Should they develop shock, they will enter decompensation very quickly. The paramedic needs to be diligent in preparation for sudden decline in patient status.

  — Describe the role of hypersecretion of corticosteroids in *Cushing's syndrome*. These patients present with a typical habitus (puffy face, obese trunk, very thin extremities) that makes them easy to identify. The EMT needs to remember that iatrogenic Cushing's syndrome also is encountered often in patients who require antirejection medications for organ transplants or need large, ongoing dosing of steroids (prednisone, Solu-Medrol) for chronic lung conditions, particularly asthma.

— Discuss androgen secretion from the adrenal cortex. In normal situations, the adrenal cortex makes a minute amount of testosterone. However, in chronically abnormal functioning of the reproductive system, the adrenal cortex's testosterone secretion can be very significant, yielding masculine physical characteristics in the female patient. The EMS professional needs to remember that this is a possible sign of much more significant disease.

- Adrenal medulla. This is the endocrine gland with which most EMT's are familiar due to the secretion of norepinephrine and epinephrine. Explain that the adrenal medulla has only a finite amount of these essential hormones, hence our need to supply additional endocrine resources during critical patient care.

g. Kidneys. Remind students that the kidneys are important regulators of both blood pressure and formed element production and that this regulation uses hormones as the information conduit.

- Explain that erythropoietin controls the rate of production for all formed elements (red and white blood cells and platelets) by the bone marrow. A synthetic form has been used successfully to combat the anemia that often accompanies chemotherapy. It has also been used, albeit illegally, to improve athletic performance, particularly by runners and cyclists. Since its release is largely stimulated by hypoxia, its oversecretion in the setting of chronic lung disease makes the blood increasingly viscous, thereby increasing the workload of the heart. This is what causes the heart failure that eventually accompanies lung disease.

- Describe the chain reaction that increases blood pressure and volume when renin is secreted within the kidney. Since the kidneys cannot function without adequate perfusion, they are in direct control of regulating systemic perfusion.

h. Heart. Discuss aldosterone and antidiuretic hormone as mechanisms that combat the nephron's tendency to excrete too much water. Explain the many ways that blood pressure consequently can become too high. An antagonist to this hypertension is atrial natriuretic hormone, secreted by the walls of the atrium, as a response to overstretching. The importance to the EMS provider to this complex system of blood pressure regulation is to fully understand the short- and long-term damage that hypertension can create. Also, one of the most important jobs paramedics can do for the patient is supporting perfusion. The better they understand how the body does this job, the better they will know how to support these systems when they fail.

i. Pancreas. Explain that hyposecretion of insulin creates a diabetic mellitus patient, while hypersecretion of insulin predisposes a patient to hypoglycemia. It is unknown why the beta cells (site of insulin production) are more susceptible to disease and destruction than the alpha cells (site of glucagon production). Discuss why synthetic glucagon can be helpful as a second-line treatment to hypoglycemia and why the success of glucagon administration is based on available glycogen stores, which cannot be assumed in the brittle diabetic patient.

j. Reproductive hormones: Briefly note the roles of reproductive hormones and explain that they are better emphasized in discussing reproductive tissues, so that EMS providers can better picture these disorders' presentation.

CHAPTER 12

Blood

INTRODUCTION

The EMT's most important job after establishing a patent airway is stopping any significant hemorrhage and supporting the functions of the blood as much as possible. The knowledge of the blood's functions will help the EMT not only to better manage the hemorrhaging patient, but also to anticipate further complications from the initial or ongoing blood loss.

LECTURE NOTES AND TEACHING STRATEGIES

Note: Now is an excellent time to reiterate blood-borne pathogen risks, particularly stating statistics from your local jurisdiction. Also pertinent are any available data regarding needle-stick injuries, new safety devices, and other body-substance isolation issues. Updated OSHA and CDC guidelines are excellent resources for current and topical data.

Start the lecture by pointing out how little blood we actually have within our bodies at any one time. Five liters of blood in the average adult represents only 7.5% of our total body weight, and only 12.5% of our total body water. We lose sight of this fact, particularly in EMS, when we so often see patients survive after losing significant amounts of blood. Also, we compare patients who lose large volumes of blood over a long period of time who function much closer to homeostasis than the patient who loses much less blood, but too quickly for their body to compensate.

1. **Plasma proteins**—Briefly introducing fluid pressures (hydrostatic vs. oncotic) is a good basis for explaining why kidney or other diseases that cause decreased plasma proteins can lead to peripheral edema as fluid flows uncontrolled into the interstitial spaces.

2. Formed elements

a. Review the concept of polycythemia in chronic hypoxic conditions, reiterating the source and function of erythropoietin. Note that the production of formed elements, while highly efficient, still takes time (5–7 days, on average). Consequently, supporting a hypovolemic patient during the initial posthemorrhage period until the body can take care of itself is a critical component of patient care.

b. Explain that the EMT will see many patients with blood disorders, ranging from the mild (thalassemia minor and sickle cell trait) to severe (leukemia, multiple anemias). Understanding their mechanisms will help support the abnormal functioning of these diseases.

c. Discuss the EMT's occasional role in continuing patient care after the patient is delivered to the emergency department. Being knowledgeable about the various lab tests being requested and performed (type, cross match, hematocrit, and hemoglobin levels, white count with differential, etc.) will build on the paramedics' understanding of their patients acutely and in the future.

d. Explain the formed elements originating from the bone marrow: Most of the healthy adult's marrow is quiescent, or "yellow," with only a few flat bones containing actively functioning, or "red" marrow. However, since these bones are often injured in trauma, particularly the ribs and pelvis, during the healing of the bone the marrow will be converted naturally from red to yellow in order to preserve that bone's nutritional reserves. Consequently, other areas are converted to fully functional state to compensate for the lost blood cell production. This does not affect the acute trauma patient but may be a factor in the initial postinjury period. The critical care transport paramedic could frequently encounter patients in this recovery period.

e. Discuss the increasing frequency of patients exhibiting severe sickle cell anemia in urban EMS systems. Use slides of sickled cells to illustrate how the clumping occurs and the process by which the aggregated cells can lead to severe pain, occlusion, and even infarction of systemic tissues.

f. Explain hemoglobin's affinity for carbon monoxide. Since hemoglobin binds with carbon monoxide 250 times more aggressively than it binds oxygen, carbon monoxide exposure can cause an insidious hypoxia. It is important to note that carbon monoxide is a product of all combustion, beyond the suicide attempt with the car running in a garage. Even EMS providers have been significantly affected by carbon monoxide sitting in a running ambulance while covering a professional standby or providing ongoing rehab treatment to the firefighters at a fire scene. Aggressive oxygen therapy, possibly even hyperbaric delivery, combined with carefully monitored carbon dioxide therapy can reverse most adverse effects of short-term exposure to carbon monoxide.

3. **Platelets/Hemostasis**

Discuss the basics of the clotting process. Aggressive hemorrhage control with only direct pressure, elevation of injury site, and pressure-point control is almost all that is needed in even a huge injury. If EMTs understand the clotting process, then they will understand how to support it. For instance, platelets become activated when coming in contact with a rough surface; therefore, the dressing applied to the injury site becomes an integral part of the clot itself. Removal or disruption of the dressing, then, will not only destroy the clot's stability but may make further hemostasis much more difficult due to the loss of the platelets that formed the first clot. Appropriate hemorrhage control upon initial arrival to the patient almost always makes the use of tourniquets and other last-ditch efforts unnecessary.

Point out the importance of understanding that myocardial infarction in the atherosclerotic patient may result after clots are initially activated upon contact with an irregular or foreign surface. Since EMS providers play a crucial role in the timely administration of thrombolytics to the patient by relaying critical patient information, the origin of the clot is an important piece of the information.

4. **Conclusion**—Use this opportunity to remind advanced life support EMS students of the importance of basic skills for the hemorrhaging patient. Based on the preceding lecture involving the functions of blood, remind the students that often the best care is the easiest—supporting the blood's function of sustaining body warmth by covering the patient with a blanket, elevating the feet to maintain core perfusion, and so on. The key to being a good paramedic is to be a great EMT.

CHAPTER 13

The Heart

INTRODUCTION

If paramedics understand the heart well, most of the emergency care treatment they provide will flow smoothly and they will easily tackle the majority of their patient contacts. As mentioned many times before in this manual, supporting perfusion is the primary goal of emergency medicine. Understanding the heart and its functions allows the paramedic to help it do its job as well as possible.

LECTURE NOTES AND TEACHING STRATEGIES

1. **Blood Flow:**

   Explain the EMT's need to really *own* knowledge about the flow path of blood. A good exercise is to "create" emboli in various locations and ask the students to suggest possible adverse effects from the emboli lodging in distant locations. (*Example:* a clot that forms in the left saphenous vein can flow through the heart and eventually lodge in the right lung, which will give rise to what signs and symptoms?)

2. **Heart Chambers:**

   a. Emphasize the thin walls of the atria. Explain that pericardial tamponade collapses atrial walls so that inflow of blood cannot occur. Most autopsy videos showing a pericardial tamponade emphasize enormous volumes of blood being present inside the pericardium, while even small volumes of fluid (blood or serous fluid, secondary to pericarditis) can collapse atrial chambers, especially if it enters very quickly.

   As always, an actual specimen creates the best educational experience.

54

Animal hearts can either be inexpensively acquired from local slaughter houses or ordered from specialty grocery stores. Cow hearts are particularly beneficial, since they are huge and their structures are so easily seen. A specimen of pericardium is also especially helpful to illustrate this point, since both its strength and inelasticity, which contribute to the development of the tamponade, can be appreciated upon tactile observation. Note that the pericardium and the dura mater that covers the central nervous system are virtually identical tissues, intended for the same protective functions.

b. Emphasize that 75 percent of a normal heart mass comprises the left ventricle, including the interventricular septum. When we assess perfusion, we are primarily measuring the ability of the left ventricle to perform its job.

c. Explain why elevated diastolic pressure can cause more long-term damage than elevated systolic pressures in chronic hypertension. The elevated diastolic pressures do not allow adequate rest for the ventricular muscle mass between contractions, hence its appropriate nickname, the "silent killer." Introduce the concepts of preload and afterload here, if they have not been covered in earlier courses.

3. **Coronary blood supply:** Explain that while the coronary arteries are not more prone to atherosclerosis than other arteries, their narrow lumen leads to more significant hypoperfusion to critical tissue. Point out the essential reason they fill during diastole (the pressure of systole would rupture them) and how the lunar valve leaflets protect them during systole by covering their outflow. Review the enormous oxygen requirements of the myocardium. It requires 20 percent of total body oxygen while accounting for less than 1 percent of total body weight. To meet this need the heart receives blood with the highest oxygen saturation available. Since myocardial infarctions represent one of the most frequent EMS calls, you cannot emphasize such points enough. The more

comfortable paramedics are with the heart, the better they can treat these patients, including making appropriate drug and electrical therapy choices and anticipating pathological conditions that can develop.

4. **Valvular systems:** Point out that patients with valvular disease are also frequently encountered in EMS. Discuss how murmurs, valve prolapses, and valve stenosis are created. Explain why infarctions or trauma that damage papillary muscles and/or chordae tendineae can create lethal perfusion problems. If possible demonstrate this point with a class dissection of a cardiac specimen.

5. **Congenital heart defects:** Explain that as neonatal medicine advances, more and more "high tech babies" are entering the prehospital environment. Provide a brief overview of the more commonly encountered heart abnormalities, especially septal defects and patent ductus arteriosus.

6. **Control of the heart:** Review the discussion in Chapter 4 of cardiac muscle's characteristics (elasticity, irritability, contractility, extensibility) and also introduce the heart's unique feature of automaticity. Since defibrillation was taught to the EMT at the basic level, based on the usage of automatic defibrillators, the EMS student now pursuing ALS certification should be comfortable with the rudimentary facts of this system.

Encourage class discussion to progress logically from the normal conduction system into all the possible points of failure and the expected changes in ECG. For example, ask the class, "What happens if the SA node fails?" Answers can range from the atrial tissue taking over stimulus (atrial fibrillation, atrial flutter, wandering atrial pacemaker) to the AV junction controlling the depolarization wave (junctional rhythms). The depth of this discussion will depend on whether the paramedic curriculum requires an independent dysrhythmia recognition course before, after, or concurrent with this anatomy and physiology course.

Note: A frivolous but effective teaching analogy for the cardiac conduction system is the U.S. military hierarchy. Imagine the president is the medulla, the SA node is the head of the joint chiefs of staff, the AV node is the highest ranking general in the army, with ever-lower-ranked officers down the septum, culminating with privates as each myocardial cell. During normal conditions, the privates follow the commands of their immediate superior perfectly, never questioning orders. However, when hungry and deprived of necessary nutrients, they get "cranky" and begin to misbehave, leading to slower or abnormal repolarization (ST segment changes, widened QRS). When really starved they can discharge their weapon (ectopic focus), creating an abnormal conduction pathway, thanks to automaticity (premature ventricular contraction). This can degenerate into complete anarchy (ventricular fibrillation).

7. **Heart sounds:** Generally, an adequate assessment of heart sounds and EMS do not mix, due to the noisy, chaotic logistics of the prehospital environment. Point out that in the newly expanded scope of paramedicine, a good understanding of how abnormal heart sounds develop and what the resultant pathophysiology can mean in terms of patient signs and symptoms is pertinent to the paramedic. The best teaching tools for this topic are either audio tapes of normal and abnormal heart sounds or the newly developed software programs that show animated cardiac action in normal and abnormal hearts. (A very detailed set of audio tapes has been produced by Dr. Proctor Harvey, considered the father of auscultative cardiology, and several software manufacturers are offering CD-ROMs.)

8. **Cardiac output control:** Explain that paramedics use both the Bainbridge reflex and the Frank-Starling mechanisms to increase perfusion every time they give a patient a fluid challenge. Emphasize that the rapid introduction of even small amounts of isotonic fluids can significantly increase both heart rate (Bainbridge) and ventricular contractile force

(Frank-Starling) while minimally altering the fluid volume within the vascular space. The synergistic relationship of these two reflexes can cause a dramatic, virtually instantaneous improvement in cardiac output and perfusion.

9. **Autonomic innervation:** Briefly review the roles of the nervous and endocrine systems in controlling the heart, as covered in Chapters 8, 9, and 11.

   a. Reiterate that during a physiologic emergency, the response of the sympathetic nervous system to the heart is immediate, increasing both heart rate and contractile force, therefore increasing cardiac output.

   b. Review the endocrine system's response of releasing norepinephrine and epinephrine. Point out that although it will take longer to kick in than the sympathetic nervous system's response, it will have greater long-lasting effects. Both hormones will work to increase efficiency of the cardiovascular system, enhancing adequate perfusion until the emergency is abated. EMS providers can easily relate to this effect, both by having taken care of patients in shock, and feeling the "buzz" following a challenging call.

10. **Electrolyte imbalances:** Stress that ALS providers need a deep understanding of electrolyte imbalances and how they can affect the heart. The best forum for this discussion is the dysrhythmia recognition course, but a brief overview can be presented here. Previously, EMS providers did not generally have access to the patient's electrolyte levels, so they could only speculate on possible imbalances based on ECG changes and the patient's history. However, with advance in prehospital medicine, the advent of critical care transport medics, and changes in the health care industry, more chronically ill patients are receiving regular health care at home,. Consequently, paramedics increasingly are responding to 911 calls to the homes of these patients, where they are greeted by a visiting nurse and the results of the patient's recent blood work.

CHAPTER 14

Blood Vessels and Circulation

INTRODUCTION

As has been mentioned repeatedly, supporting perfusion is one of the paramedic's primary tasks. Since a myriad of factors can adversely affect the blood vessels, this job is often easier said than done. When the medic fully understands the structure and control of the blood vessels, supporting perfusion becomes a more manageable task.

LECTURE NOTES AND TEACHING STRATEGIES

1. **Vessel structure:** Describe the structure of arteries and veins.

    a. Tunica interna—Explain that the critical feature of this layer is its normally smooth and frictionless interior. In the setting of atherosclerosis created by a high-fat and/or high-cholesterol diet, this layer becomes coated with irregular plaque. As discussed in Chapter 12, Blood, contact with any abnormal surface encourages platelet activation, creating clots. Turbulent blood flow, created by the plaque, further encourages clot formation. We now know that the obstruction of the coronary arteries by these clots is the primary cause of myocardial infarction.

    Discuss how the relatively thin and fragile innermost layer of the blood vessels is easily damaged and perhaps even torn in the event of an abrupt deceleration force or long-term severe hypertension. This vulnerability can create a dissecting aortic aneurysm as the internal tissue tears and the high-pressure introduction of blood between the layers separates the interna from the medial and adventitial layers. This emergency is life-threatening and requires aggressive EMS treatment and rapid transport to definitive care.

b. Tunica media—Describe this "business" layer of the blood vessels and discuss the critical importance of its responsiveness to both nervous and endocrine stimuli for homeostasis. Its elasticity is chronically challenged by the increased diastolic pressure of hypertension, creating arteriosclerosis, or "hardening of the arteries." The resultant loss of resiliency creates a more difficult work environment for the ventricles, encouraging hypertrophy. The enlarged muscle mass increases the oxygen requirement for the myocardium, setting up the vicious circle of congestive heart failure. It now becomes obvious to the paramedic student why these patients have such involved, extensive patient histories with accompanying long lists of supportive medications. Point out that understanding the series of events that led to their current condition helps the medic anticipate what can go wrong next.

Remind the EMT student that this middle layer is where the structural differences between arteries and veins exist. The lumen space of a vein is actually larger than that of its analogous artery, but the medial layer of the artery is much thicker and more developed, allowing for greater resistance to pressure and making the artery appear larger than the corresponding vein.

c. Tunica externa—Describe this layer's composition primarily of strong yet flexible collagen fibers and explain that it can fail either congenitally or because of the long-term abuse of hypertension. Its failure and loss of integrity becomes an aneurysm, as the blood causes bulging of the weakened blood vessel wall. An aneurysm can occur anywhere in the body; list the locations of aneurysms that cause that greatest detriment to the patient: (1) in the brain, where the rupture creates a stroke; (2) in the heart, where the rupture causes an infarction, or 3) at the bifurcation of the abdominal aorta, where constant back-pressure naturally weakens the external vessel wall. The ensuing aneurysm can become exceedingly large without the patient's knowledge, but the rupture of any aneurysm is a real life-threat. Since the development of the aneurysm is generally painless, it is important to note that the first time a patient may become aware of the vessel abnormality may be during its rapid dissection or rupture. The rupture, however, is excruciating to the patient.

2. **Vascular control—Describe and explain the following aspects of vascular control:**

   a. Autoregulation: Define this as the point of impact by histamine release upon mast cell activation by foreign antigens. When this system is stimulated on a broad scale by a hypersensitivity to the foreign antigen the response becomes an allergic reaction. If it is particularly aggressive or systemic, we call the response anaphylaxis. The massive release of histamine alters cellular permeability, making cells "leaky"; hence, the edema of anaphylaxis. The histamine's autoregulatory function is overstimulated, with the potential to create massive vasodilation, culminating in anaphylactic shock. It now becomes obvious to the paramedic student why the administration of diphenhydramine, a histamine blocker, helps manage this patient. Explain that anti-inflammatory steroids can help prevent a relapse while the allergen remains in the body.

   (1) Describe prostaglandin synthesis. Prostaglandin release becomes the stimulus for action of many NSAID medications. Explain that pain relief is gained when these medications go to the site of inflammation and block prostaglandin action, lessening the edema and increased blood flow to the site.

   (2) Discuss some of the very recent discoveries about autoregulation by nitric oxide and their potential future impact on EMS. Nitric oxide, recently named Molecule of the Year, by *Science*, has been shown to be a major player in autoregulation of perfusion at the capillary level.

Naturally occurring as a gas, its administration to critically ill patients has shown dramatic benefits, particularly to those with congenital heart defects or chronic cardiac conditions.

b. Neural control: Describe the medulla's role as the vasomotor center in reference to cerebral herniation syndrome's extreme hypertension with reflexive widened pulse pressure and resultant bradycardia. Note that this is known collectively (with respiratory abnormalities) as Cushing's Triad. Previously, it was suggested that hyperventilation was the appropriate treatment for management of head injuries, as vasoconstriction was encouraged by lowered carbon dioxide and increased oxygen levels. We now know that this mechanism is perhaps *too* effective, causing deleterious vasoconstriction and should be avoided except in the setting of herniation syndrome, an immediate life threat.

c. Baroreceptor reflexes: Discuss how we occasionally call in these reflexes to our advantage in EMS. Illustrate this with the example of performing carotid sinus massage on a patient in supraventricular tachycardia. While this practice has the potential risk of loosening thrombi within the carotid lumen or damaging the vessel itself, activating the baroreception can dramatically slow the heart's activity. (*Note:* The atrial baroreceptor function has already been discussed, in reference to its secretion of atrial natriuretic hormone, in Chapter 11.)

d. Chemoreception: Explain that chronic disruption of this very sensitive regulatory system can forever alter the system's functioning, as seen in patients with chronic lung disorders. For example, we know that patients with long-term emphysema become dependent on hypoxic drive for respiratory and cardiovascular control due to the constant disruption of the normal control system. Hypoxic drive is far inferior, in terms of ensuring perfusion, but exists as a compensatory mechanism when the normal control factors fail.

e. Autonomic and higher brain control: Explain the body's perception of emotional stress as physiologic stress. This is the phenomenon that creates hypertension in workaholic, driven-to-succeed individuals, leading them to premature cardiovascular disease.

f. Hormonal control: Describe how the pharmaceutical industry is working to help control the rampant hypertension in our society by altering the hormonal regulatory system. *Examples:* The so-called ACE (angiotensin converting enzyme) inhibitor medications have shown great success against chronically elevated blood pressure as they block the formation of angiotensin II, a potent vasoconstrictor. Another approach is through using furosemide or other "loop" diuretics, as they successfully counteract oversecreted antidiuretic hormone by encouraging water loss at the nephron.

3. **Cardiovascular response to hemorrhaging:** Discuss the controversy surrounding the use of fluid resuscitation in critical shock. Until synthetic blood replacements can be utilized easily in the prehospital environment, the paramedic's only course to aid a critical trauma patient is aggressive airway management, rapid transport, and fluid administration to help sustain perfusion. However, it has been widely suggested that massive fluid introduction to the vascular space of a patient in shock actually reverses the body's natural compensatory mechanisms, rendering the patient's condition worse rather than improved. The American Medical Association created headlines several years ago by strongly stating that fluid administration was perhaps even a life-threatening rather than life-saving action. Engage students in an open, informal conversation about this topic not only to provoke thought but also to encourages them to think about their emergency medical actions on a cellular level.

4. **Shock:** Discuss in depth the cellular aspects of shock. EMS students need to be very comfortable with this topic in order to truly understand why their shock patients need the most comprehensive yet rapid care. Reiterate that shock and airway are universally the highest priorities in patient care (except in the case of ventricular fibrillation, where initiation of defibrillation takes precedence), so a comprehensive knowledge of shock's pathophysiological mechanisms is essential.

    a. Review the main factors that create the different shock types:

        (1) Septic:

            (a) Quality of blood is poor, containing high levels of toxins created by pathogenic metabolism.

            (b) Presence of toxins causes vasodilation.

            (c) Hypovolemia is caused by inadequate intake and increased water loss due to high respirations and sweat resulting from recurrent febrile episodes.

        (2) Hypovolemia: Volume is lost by hemorrhage or third-space loss, such as extensive burns. (The stages of shock are discussed in detail in the next section.)

        (3) Respiratory:

            (a) Quality of blood is poor, characterized by hypoxemia and/or hypercarbia.

            (b) Respiratory shock usually occurs secondary to thoracic trauma, respiratory infection, or chronic pulmonary condition.

        (4) Metabolic: Quality of blood is poor and inadequate to sustain perfusion due to errors of glucose metabolism or accumulations of metabolic byproducts, as in anorexia nervosa or other gastrointestinal disorders.

(5)   Psychogenic: An abnormal response to emotional stress causes transient but massive vasodilation, resulting in syncope. While this usually presents merely as "fainting," it can be extreme, with the complications of the syncope becoming life threatening.

(6)   Cardiogenic: Cardiogenic shock results from failure of the system's pump, usually secondary to massive myocardial infarction, cardiac insufficiency due to myocardial hypertrophy, or exacerbation of congenital heart defects (for example, right to left shunting through a septal defect).

(7)   Anaphylactic: Hypersensitivity to an allergen causes massive mast cell activation, creating histamine release. Histamine creates fluid shifts away from vascular space, in turn causing edema, representing third-space fluid loss. Toxins of reaction accumulate, encouraging vasodilation. Possible accompanying bronchoconstriction exacerbates this condition by ensuing hypoxia.

(8)   Neurogenic: Failure of the neural control component causes vasodilation as vascular tone is lost. This usually occurs secondary to spinal or head injury.

b. Define the stages of shock and list their characteristics:

    (1)   Compensated shock:

        (a)   Heart rate and force of contraction increase, due first to autonomic, and later, to endocrine factors.

        (b)   Respiratory rate increases to improve oxygen levels in the blood.

        (c)   Peripheral vasoconstriction shunts blood to the core. Systemic vasoconstriction increases blood pressure.

(d)   Platelets aggregate to the site of vessel rupture, initiating the clotting cascade.

(e)   Fluid shifts from interstitial to vascular space.

(2)   Decompensated shock:

(a)   Heart and respiratory rates continue to increase beyond the point of efficacy.

(b)   Catecholamine levels, particularly norepinephrine, are exhausted, so blood vessels lose constrictive tone.

(c)   Blood pressure drops, due to vasodilation and venous pooling.

(d)   Products of anaerobic metabolism accumulate, decreasing blood pH.

(e)   Microemboli form systemically due to stagnant blood.

(f)   The sodium pump fails due to unavailable ATP and allows sodium into cells. Fluid accompanies sodium and migrates from vascular space into cells, causing cells to swell.

(g)   Cells in the periphery begin to die due to inadequate blood supply.

(3)   Irreversible shock:

(a)   Cell membranes fail, with their rupture releasing bradykinins and histamine. These potent enzymes then cause massive vasodilation and lysosomic enzymes furthering tissue damage.

(b)   Microemboli migrate to lungs, causing pulmonary emboli and encouraging pulmonary edema. Inadequate tidal volume causes atelectasis (adult respiratory distress syndrome).

(c)   The patient develops both respiratory and metabolic acidosis, lowering blood pH dangerously below the homeostatic range.

(d)   Fluid continues to shift into inappropriate sites, causing more third-space loss.

(e)   Massive multiple hemorrhages occur throughout the body as platelet levels are exhausted (disseminated intravascular coagulation).

(f)   Vital organs fail, causing malignant dysrhythmias, seizures, acute kidney failure, and pulmonary infarction.

(g)   Death occurs regardless of interventions.

5. **Specific blood vessels:** Review with EMS students all available pulse sites for more thorough patient assessment. Review sites of arteries in extremities for pressure point use in hemorrhage control. Explain how congestive heart failure leads to hepatomegaly, based on the back pressure of flow within the inferior vena cava through the liver. More or less class time may be spent on identifying blood vessels, based on need. If possible, illustrate this lesson with large diagrams and human specimen.

6. **Fetal circulation:** Identify all four fetal circulatory bypasses and explain how and why they exist. Discuss how the child would present if the closure of these bypasses failed to occur. In addition to these normal circulation alterations, a myriad of congenital failures can occur. As detection of these congenital defects in utero has advanced, the number of infants who survive such abnormalities has increased. These children are now frequent consumers of emergency medical services. Explain the paramedic's need to understand management of these potentially critical patients and their unique vascular systems.

CHAPTER 15

The Lymphatic System and Immunity

INTRODUCTION

The EMT students have become aware of two important facts since the onset of their training:

1. Their primary responsibility on any scene is to protect themselves, first and foremost.

2. Innumerable pathogens exist to which they are at risk, and these pathogens have an infinite ability to mutate, becoming stronger and more drug resistant.

A clearer understanding of how the body protects itself against these pathogens should give EMTs a stronger sense of how to take better care both of themselves and of their infected patients.

LECTURE NOTES AND TEACHING STRATEGIES

1. **Review the basics of this system.** Illuminate the structure and function of lymphatic tissue.

   a. Note that the lymphatic and vascular systems run in parallel tracks throughout the body. This supports one of the lymphatic system's most essential functions, the return of interstitial fluid to circulation. While this amounts to only about 3 liters per day, its failure can lead to massive and potentially debilitating edema. Remember that severe edema can obstruct critical tissues, such as arteries, veins, and nerves. Discuss how this might affect patient assessment.

   b. Illustrate areas of the body where lymph nodes are clustered, emphasizing the importance of checking for enlarged and inflamed lymphatic tissue during patient assessment. The swollen glands of systemic infection indicate a lymphatic system doing its job.

    c. Point out how cancer cells utilize the lymphatic vessels for transportation to distant locations elsewhere in the body. EMS professionals care for cancer patients often, so understanding that lymphatic involvement indicates metastasis of the tumor can help with patient management. The metastatic growth can exacerbate the patient's condition dramatically, and the paramedic should know common metastatic pathways in order to help prepare for further complications. For example, breast cancer often migrates to the brain; therefore; a breast cancer patient, where cancer cells were found in the lymph nodes of the breast, may have metastasis to the brain, and altered mentation and seizures should be anticipated. Similarly, because of testicular cancer's potential spread to the lungs, the paramedic should anticipate respiratory compromise.

2. Discuss the spleen and its significance in emergency care.

    a. The spleen is the most commonly injured organ in abdominal trauma. Not only is it highly vascular, but it also consists of a relatively fragile tissue. Consequently, it heals poorly, and attempting to suture or repair it after injury is very difficult and largely unsuccessful. Since the spleen is not a vital organ, it is often removed post-trauma. The paramedic should remember that the post-splenectomy patient is therefore at greater risk for opportunistic infection. The liver will eventually take over many of the spleen's functions, should the spleen be removed, but the patient is especially vulnerable in the acute postoperative period.

    b. Since one of the spleen's functions is to monitor and remove abnormal cells from the blood stream, it naturally enlarges when a systemic infection is present. This is particularly noted in certain diseases such as leukemia and mononucleosis, where the spleen can grow up to 10 times its normal size. The resultant splenomegaly puts the patient at increased risk of splenic injury in trauma. The paramedic should note any pertinent medical history in these patients and have greater suspicion for possible splenic injury and hemorrhage.

c. The spleen also can enlarge dangerously when engulfing large numbers of other formed elements, such as erythrocytes, in conditions such as sickle cell crisis. The spleen recognizes the sickled cells as abnormal and engulfs them in mass quantities. An emergency splenectomy is sometimes required in an acute situation.

d. The spleen naturally atrophies in old age, contributing to the increased risk of infection in the geriatric patient.

3. **Describe the tonsils and explain their role in prehospital care.**

a. The tonsils are now known to provide important immune protection to the pharynx and upper airway, significantly decreasing the frequency of required tonsillectomies since the 1950s and 1960s, when this surgical removal was very common.

b. Enlargement of the tonsils, while a normal occurrence in upper respiratory infections, can be massive, potentially obstructing the airway. However, because of the delicate tissue and the difficulty negotiating around the tonsils, endotracheal intubation should be a last resort for airway management. The use of humidified oxygen, positioning for optimal airway compliance and possible administration of nebulized medications will be adequate in most instances.

4. **Explain the thymus and T cell formation.** Some of the factors that lead to AIDS infection involve the thymus gland. The thymus is largely atrophied by adulthood. Since, T cells are the most vulnerable to attack and alteration by human immunodeficiency virus (HIV) and the thymus's function decreased, the AIDS patient has severe vulnerability to opportunistic infection.

5. Explain the body's barriers and other protective factors.

    a. Personal health care—The best defense is a good offense. The most successful way to avoid illness is to have a healthy body. This includes many factors, from adequate rest, nutrition, and exercise, with lessened stress, to adequate maintenance for chronic conditions, such as diabetes, hypertension, and hyperlipidemia. In EMS, this is easier said than done; however, it cannot be stressed enough that EMTs need to take superb care of themselves, for their own sake and for their patients' sake. They also have a responsibility as public role models, in terms of physical fitness, nutrition, and health maintenance. EMTs should find out what diseases and vaccines they acquired in childhood or have their antibody levels (titer) tested for adequate immunity to know which infections from patients pose their greatest risk.

    b. Skin—It is well known that having intact skin provides one of the most critical elements of resistance to infection. However, few professions are as hard on the skin as EMS. Take a few moments to have students examine their hands, noting the raw, dry skin from overwashing, the scrapes from their last vehicle extrication training exercise, the torn calluses from lifting the heavy cot and physical fitness training. Remind them that any loss of integrity of the skin increases their vulnerability to pathogens significantly. This is a good reminder about the use of lubricants after hand washing, the use of gloves during patient contacts, and the general need to take better care of themselves.

    c. Acquired immunity—EMS professionals should take as many precautions as possible against their nearly constant exposure to pathogens. This means that they should take full advantage of the vaccines available to them: hepatitis B, pneumonia, and chicken pox vaccinations, annual flu shots, and any others. These vaccines have shown great success with minimal risk. Regular screening for tuberculosis also provides some protection, in that the EMT will most likely be unaware of any exposure and early medication administration will often prevent the disease from developing.

6. **Consider immune disorders and allergic responses.**

   a. Autoimmune disorders—An increasing number of disorders are being found to involve, in whole or in part, an autoimmune dysfunction, where self tissue is not recognized appropriately. These disorders' effects range from mild to severely debilitating, such as lupus, rheumatoid arthritis, multiple sclerosis, and type I diabetes mellitus. It has been hypothesized that the prevalence of industrial chemicals in our world is perhaps encouraging this phenomenon and that with information gained from the Human Genome Project and advances in genetic engineering, the numbers of known autoimmune-induced disorders will probably soar. It is important to note that the autoimmune response is enhanced by both steroidal anti-inflammatory medications and increased stress, factors that paramedics will see often in patients and perhaps in themselves, as well.

   b. Allergies—The allergic response is very similar to the immune reaction, except that the stimulating factor is a foreign antigen, or allergen, rather than a pathogen. Similar to autoimmune disorders, allergies are also dramatically on the rise, attributed largely to our chemically overstimulated environment. Severe systemic reactions, known as anaphylaxis, are being seen in ever-increasing numbers in the pediatric population and should be always considered a potential life-threat.

   Paramedics should remember that with each exposure the patient's allergic response will become progressively more acute and systemic and that anaphylaxis can develop very rapidly. These facts should spur the medic to anticipate such complications as bronchoconstriction, laryngospasm, and vascular collapse and to prepare for aggressive resuscitation.

7. **Describe the effects of aging on immunity.** Due to a myriad of factors, the geriatric patient not only is very susceptible to opportunistic infections but also is less able to compensate for these infections. Combined with probable chronic health conditions, this makes managing the geriatric patient even more difficult.

For example, compare a 30-year-old patient and a 75 –year-old patient with possible pneumonia. Both are very ill and have the potential for serious complications. The younger patient will probably present with fever, malaise, dehydration, and mild respiratory distress, with a productive cough. The older patient will have these same problems, as well as a probable cardiac condition and history of previous respiratory infections. This patient is perhaps chronically dehydrated, so the increased fluid loss of sepsis may make her dangerously hypovolemic. Any fluid resuscitation could encourage heart failure. The accumulated toxins from the infection and sustained hypoxia can illicit malignant dysrhythmias, dementia, and seizures. Moreover, they have a combined risk for respiratory and septic shock. Any pharmacological agents used may react adversely with therapeutic medications these patients take on a daily basis. In infection, as well as in other pathological conditions, managing the geriatric patient can be an especially challenging task.

CHAPTER 16

The Respiratory System

INTRODUCTION

"Airway, airway, airway!"

The average paramedic student can recall hearing this motto in virtually every EMS class he or she has ever attended. Earlier in this course, we have discussed the cellular importance of readily available oxygen. We have also mentioned many times the paramedic's essential role of supporting perfusion in all patient care scenarios. If our definition of perfusion is "oxygenated blood being delivered to every body cell," the need to appreciate all elements of the respiratory system is obvious. Also, when a paramedic understands the normal structure and function of a tissue, treating abnormal presentations and anticipating their potential complications will be easier.

LECTURE NOTES AND TEACHING STRATEGIES

1. **Describe the anatomical structures of the respiratory system:**

    a. Nasopharynx—Explain that the turbinates encourage slower airflow into the lungs but pose a structural obstacle to both nasopharyngeal airways and nasotracheal intubation. Point out how very vascular the turbinates are and that overaggressive airway placement can create dangerous epistaxis. Explain that all humans breathe primarily through the nose and that infants are obligate nose-breathers, so trauma or medical conditions that affect nasal tissue can potentially cause respiratory compromise.

    b. Oral cavity—Discuss the ways in which broken teeth, emesis, blood, and edema of the tongue and other structures can severely obstruct the airway and encourage aspiration. Describe how appropriate suctioning and head placement can aid in most situations. Ongoing training in endotracheal intubation is necessary to perform this often difficult skill. Note that hypoxia is occasionally an unavoidable side effect of suctioning, and that bradycardia and acidosis can be the byproducts of this hypoxia.

c. Sinuses—Explain that while sinus infections by themselves rarely pose a serious life-threat, if left untreated they can develop into meningitis and sepsis, which are more commonly encountered by EMS.

d. Epiglottis—Describe the epiglottis's life-saving reflex of closing when foreign material enters the pharynx. Discuss the many factors that can interfere with this reflex, such as alcohol intoxication, drug ingestion, and head injury. Any patient with a significant decrease in level of consciousness should be considered to have lost this protection, until proven otherwise, by intact action of the gag reflex. Remind students that the epiglottis must be open for air to enter the trachea. Therefore, a hypoxic patient's epiglottis may not perform normally. Explain that the need for oxygen can override the need to protect the trachea.

e. Tracheal/esophageal positioning—Note the proximity of these two structures. Point out that the posterior aspect of the trachea is covered only with smooth muscle and that the cartilaginous rings are C-shaped. This allows the esophagus to "borrow" room from the trachea as the bolus of food passes to the stomach. Hence, a particularly large food bolus can obstruct the trachea without actually being in the airway. Explain that the Heimlich maneuver will correct this problem by increasing the intrathoracic pressure enough to expel the material. A significant number of ailments and medications can also cause esophageal malfunctioning, delaying passage of food into the stomach. The food bolus's extended presence in the esophagus can affect both respiratory and cardiac function.

f. Alveoli—Discuss the vast number of alveoli and relate it to chest decompression in pneumothorax. Paramedic students are understandably nervous about performing this important skill, partially in fear of damaging healthy lung tissue. When the medic inserts the needle into the chest cavity, healthy tissue could indeed be damaged. Explain, however, that the alveolar destruction that might be caused will heal readily and allowing any trapped air to escape is essential for homeostasis.

Show students actual specimens. If human teaching cadavers are not available, local slaughterhouses or butchers will usually donate animal airways for this purpose. Sheep, pig, or calf organs are approximately human-sized, and therefore will accommodate human endotracheal tubes and give a great demonstration with adult bag-valve-mask ventilations. Usually, new medics who have practiced chest decompression on animal specimens are much less hesitant to do the "real thing" in the patient with serious thoracic trauma.

2.   Explain respiratory physiology.

a. Review the mechanics of breathing and pulmonary circulation. This helps paramedic students comprehend the pathophysiology of congestive heart failure, adult respiratory distress syndrome, pulmonary embolus, hemothorax, and pneumothorax.

This is hopefully an important turning point for budding medics, as they begin to "put it all together." The crux of these learning moments is when the medic associates a failed organ with its potential impact on other organs. For example, a myocardial infarction involving the left ventricle may lead not only to inadequate systemic circulation but failure to pull fluids out of the lung, encouraging fluid backup into the lungs, forcing fluid across alveolar membranes. These fluid-filled air sacs are now unavailable for gas exchange, encouraging further hypoxemia, which may lead to another infarct—and the vicious circle continues. In EMS we see these patients almost every day, so the medic needs not only to treat the patient's current condition, but also to anticipate further declines that could occur.

b. Explain that inspiration is an active process, while expiration is passive, with air leaving the body merely by relaxation of the respiratory muscles. Consequently, patients in respiratory distress, particularly asthmatics, can inhale easier than they can exhale, and air is trapped in the lungs. Since asthma patients can now do so much of their care at home, 911 may not be activated until the patient is in extremis. Discuss the many problems and obstacles to their care presented by this increased air volume trapped in their lungs.

c. Describe the role of accessory muscles in respiration. While normal respiration is based mostly on the action of the diaphragm, and to a much lesser degree, the intercostal muscles, additional muscles can be recruited in times of need. The accessory muscles of respiration can include the sternocleidomastoids, the pectorals, the abdominals, and the trapezius. Stress that whenever accessory muscle use is noted, the medic should assume the patient's airway is in dire straits and prepare for aggressive airway assistance. The recruitment of these large muscles also increases the fatigue of respiratory distress.

3. Explain respiratory control: Summarize the mechanisms by which the respiratory drive functions, based on chemoreception. Describe the precise efficiency of the measuring of carbon dioxide in the blood and of determining respiratory rate, rhythm, and depth from this concentration. Explain that the subsystem in which oxygen concentration determines these factors is far less effective. Remind students that the majority of carbon dioxide travels as carbonic acid in the bloodstream, giving the lungs a primary role in controlling acid-base balance. In fact, the respiratory system is the body's first-line action in

maintaining homeostatic pH:

$$\uparrow\text{resp.} = \downarrow CO_2 = \downarrow\text{carbonic acid} = \uparrow\text{pH}$$

Point out that the renal system's further control over pH abnormalities is more effective and longer lasting, but the respiratory system's ability to kick in immediately is life-saving.

4. **Review respiratory diseases:** Presumably, the frequently seen chronic respiratory diseases, such as emphysema, asthma, and cystic fibrosis, will be covered in other courses. Reiterate important points regarding assessment and treatment of these diseases, which constitute a significant portion of emergency medicine.

CHAPTER 17

The Digestive System

INTRODUCTION

There are two main reasons that EMS professionals need to understand the digestive system:

1. To better take care of themselves. If the adage "you are what you eat," is really true, then the average paramedic is in dire straits. The infamous EMS diet is rarely nutritionally sound, putting the medic at risk for all types of digestive disorders, not to mention obesity and cardiovascular disease. Since the first and foremost responsibility of the EMT is to him/herself, then the digestive system should be a high personal priority.

2. Disorders of the digestive system often lead to nausea and vomiting, an absolute risk to the patient's airway, our highest treatment priority. The management of these patients most often is merely "O_2, IV, monitor, position of comfort, and rapid transport" and seldom requires any of the medic's vast knowledge of cardiology or pharmacology. Although these are not the most challenging patient care interactions, no machine runs well when something is wrong with its fuel supply, so understanding this system is important for all patient care.

LECTURE NOTES AND TEACHING STRATEGIES

1. **Discuss the oral cavity.** Note that all the structures of the oral cavity are highly vascular. Consequently, any damage due to trauma can cause significant hemorrhage into the oropharynx with possible airway compromise. Also, broken teeth and torn tissues can easily become airway obstructions. Patients with facial trauma can be very difficult to manage.

Explain that hypoxia can sometimes cause serious swelling of the tongue, particularly in anaphylaxis and acute respiratory conditions, such as asthma. This edema can make orotracheal, and perhaps even nasotracheal intubation difficult, if not impossible. Paramedics will rarely need to create a surgical airway during their EMS careers, but they need to practice this life-saving skill and be as comfortable with it as possible if the need for it ever arises.

2. **Describe the esophagus.** Its proximity and "space-sharing" feature has already been discussed in the respiratory chapter. Many conditions and medications can disrupt normal functioning, causing slowed peristalsis moving the food bolus to the stomach. Patients sometimes perceive the lodged bolus of food as an airway obstruction and activate EMS. The EMT does not need to worry about the differential diagnosis, but rather must work to clear the airway, if needed. The Heimlich maneuver can still be effective.

   a. Explain the lower esophageal sphincter of the stomach. It is located at the distal end of the esophagus, where the esophagus passes through the hiatus, or opening in the diaphragm. This sphincter can fail, usually caused by pressure from an enlarged stomach, by medications, or by other physical conditions. Its failure results in "heartburn," otherwise known as gastric reflux, as stomach contents can pass retroactively up the esophagus. Damage can be done to the delicate tissues of the esophagus, since it lacks the protective defense mechanisms against the very potent gastric enzymes. This type of reflux can be a temporary condition, caused by pregnancy or a patient's temporary need to spend a large amount of time in a supine position (recovering from a pelvic or femoral fracture, for example). It can also be a chronic problem caused by obesity or eating a large meal late at night and then lying supine in bed.

   b. Discuss hiatal hernias. Hiatal hernias occur when the sphincter is so weakened by any of the above conditions that a portion of the stomach can actually pass through the opening to rest above the diaphragm. Again, this can be a temporary problem, so when the patient sits or stands, gravity assists and allows the organs to fall into their normal position. If it persists, permanent damage can occur to both the stomach and the diaphragm. Patients with a hiatal hernia are in extreme pain and may activate 911. The medic may have a difficult time with the differential diagnosis, as this disorder can mimic almost perfectly a myocardial infarction, particularly of the inferior wall. Making the diagnosis is not critical, however, since most treatment given to the heart attack patient will benefit the hiatal hernia patient as well. Definitive care may require surgical repair at this point.

3. **Discuss the stomach.** The muscular functions of the stomach are explained well in the text. These are the same contractions that can create forceful reverse contractions, causing vomiting or emesis. The stimulus may be local irritation of the stomach by alcohol ingestion, overdose of oral medications, or the presence of a pathogen, as in food poisoning. The stimulus also can originate from the emesis center of the brain, and some frequently used EMS medications, such as morphine or Demerol, are notorious for causing this type of emesis. Fortunately, an antiemetic, such as Phenergan or Vistaril, can block this reaction at the brain.

   a. Explain that ischemia to the brain due to head injury can also cause this effect, resulting in dramatic projectile vomiting, an immediate risk to a patent airway.

   b. Explain that systemic hypoperfusion causing ischemia to the digestive tract can create emesis, as a significant fluid volume is necessary for normal digestion. The body in shock recognizes that homeostatic fluid volumes are not available; hence, normal digestion cannot occur. By ridding itself of excess food, the body will prevent future potentially life-threatening complications, such as bowel obstruction.

The paramedic needs to be prepared for aggressive suctioning and intubation in these cases.

4. **Discuss the liver.** The liver is the second largest organ in the body and also one of the most vascular (containing approximately 25 percent of total blood volume). Stress that the liver is also the second most commonly injured abdominal organ in trauma. A liver laceration can cause exsanguination in a matter of moments. The medic needs to be suspicious of this injury in any decelerating, penetrating, or blunt-force trauma, particularly when resulting in shock. Kerr's sign, where pain radiates to the shoulders from abdominal palpation, may help with the diagnosis, but the mechanism of injury is always the best indicator of suspicion for damage to this vital organ.

   Point out that although the liver has an amazing array of functions, its malfunctions do not often present in emergency medical care. Sadly, the many drug- and alcohol-addicted patients seen in EMS abuse the liver's detoxification function. Although the ensuing cirrhosis does not incite many 911 calls, the resultant jaundice should always get the attention of the EMT. While infectious hepatitis is not always the cause of jaundice, the health care worker should routinely be cautious and utilize body-substance isolation during these patient contacts.

5. **Explain the gall bladder.** Cholecystitis, or a gall bladder attack, can be a common 911 emergency. Its presentation is often sudden onset during sleep in a supine position, and the abdominal pain it causes can be excruciating. The diagnosis can be tricky, again mimicking a myocardial infarction or hiatal hernia. The actual condition does not pose an immediate life threat, but aggressive care is still indicated due to the extreme pain, along with the hypertension and tachycardia that the pain can cause. Patients can have repeated episodes of cholecystitis, as gall stones migrate in and out of the common bile duct. When the stones recede back into the gall bladder, the pain is instantly abated. History

becomes critical to this diagnosis, and while a majority of patients will fit into the "fat, female, forty" group, a patient of any age, shape, or gender can have this condition.

6. **Discuss the small intestine.** A large number of chronic conditions of the small intestine, many involving malabsorption, exist. Examples of these maladies are Crohn's disease, irritable bowel syndrome, and ulcerative colitis. These patients do not often need emergency assistance, but since they may present with persistent diarrhea, dangerous dehydration, and subsequent syncope, they may call 911.

7. **Explain the appendix.** Generally considered a vestigial organ, the appendix has no known function in the human being. However, in a small group of people, fecal material can lodge inside its narrow lumen, and the enclosed bacteria can proliferate, causing swelling and irritation. This inflammation can migrate into the surrounding tissues, causing peritonitis and the infamous rebound tenderness indicative of appendicitis. While appendicitis is unlikely to cause an acute medical emergency that requires EMS involvement, the potential exists for the appendix to rupture, which in turn can be life-threatening.

8. **Discuss the large intestine.** A major complaint among geriatric patients involves problems with the large intestine. Explain the dangerous combination of factors that play into these chronic conditions:

    a. The geriatric patient usually eats a bland, low-fiber diet, which is easier to chew and swallow but encourages slow, weak, and less effective peristalsis.

    b. The geriatric patient is often chronically dehydrated, so that less body water is available for digestion, creating chronically hard and dry fecal masses.

    c. Most medications for heart and blood pressure problems are constipating in nature.

    d. These factors add up to a high predisposition for impaction, bowel obstruction, and possibly even bowel rupture. Add any tendency toward diverticulitis or colitis, and the result may be disastrous. Colon cancer is also a leading cause of death for the geriatric patient. The medic must be aware of these potential risks, to better manage the older patient.

CHAPTER 18

Nutrition and Metabolism

INTRODUCTION

Many chronic medical conditions and medications can alter a patient's metabolism. While this does not play a large role in the acute condition that has led to EMS involvement, it does predispose these patients to hypothermia and hyperthermia, altered level of consciousness, and shock. For example, the unrestrained driver involved in a serious MVA, with a history of hypothyroidism, may develop shock from a lacerated liver much more aggressively and faster than would an otherwise healthy patient. The medic who anticipates this dangerous decline is getting the next best thing to a crystal ball.

LECTURE NOTES AND TEACHING STRATEGIES

1. **Explain cellular metabolism.** Review the critical need for available oxygen to supply the cellular mechanisms for energy production. The primary fuel substrate, glucose, is equally important. Luckily, our body can break down a vast array of food products into glucose, so that a balanced diet supplies all we need. Remind students of the concurrent need for appropriate hormone levels in order to get the fuel into the cells.

   a. Carbohydrates—Explain that under normal conditions our body is an amazing machine, converting complex structures into simple glucose molecules, mobilizing only what is needed, and saving the rest in the form of glycogen for storage and potential later use. This system runs beautifully in normal situations, but if necessary hormonal control is lost or insufficient, problems such as diabetes mellitus occur. The paramedic will become very familiar with the presentation of hypoglycemia, as it is a very common EMS occurrence. Explain that the glycogen stores are routinely depleted in these patients, so that raising blood glucose levels by glucagon administration is unpredictable.

  b. Lipids—Point out that our body is almost as efficient at breaking down fats as it is carbohydrates. Explain the importance of lipids as an essential building block in the body's formation of myelin and other insulating tissue. Critical fat stores protect vital organs, such as the heart and kidneys. Note that the average American diet is far too high in carbohydrates and lipids, which leads to obesity, hypertension, and atherosclerosis, but a diet with inadequate lipid intake is dangerous as well.

  c. Proteins—Explain that more energy is required for protein breakdown than for either carbohydrate or lipid metabolism. The resultant amino acids are necessary for tissue repair, hormone production, and pathogen defense. A diet too rich in protein can damage the kidneys. If proteins are the only available fuel, such as in diabetes-induced hyperglycemia, the acidic byproducts accumulate in excessive amounts, causing systemic metabolic acidosis. The patient compensates by creating respiratory alkalosis, with extreme hyperventilation, or Kussmaul's respirations.

2. **Nutrition.** Remind students that the classic EMS diet is ridiculously high in complex carbohydrates, lipids, and caffeine and dangerously low in protein, vitamins, fruits, vegetables, and free water. The main point of this lecture should be for students to assess their own diet and consider how it can be improved. A healthier medic can take better care of patients, after all.

3. **Metabolism.** Discuss the number of medications, normal and abnormal patient conditions, and diseases that can alter the body's metabolism. For example, pregnancy and lactation dramatically alter a woman's normal metabolism. If you add trauma or an infection to the mix, the resultant *very* abnormal metabolism can cause serious complications. Medications such as antibiotics, antipsychotics, and treatments for malaria

or viral infections all increase metabolism significantly. Illicit drugs such as hallucinogenics, amphetamines, or other stimulants increase metabolism, while barbiturates and sedatives lessen it.

Explain the significance of an increased metabolic rate in EMS. Perhaps it means a diet-controlled, borderline diabetic is now in seizure, with a blood sugar level of 15 mg/dL, needing emergency care. Or a patient with Grave's Disease may be in thyroid storm stimulated by a case of strep throat, presenting with malignant hypertension, extreme tachycardia, and a dangerously elevated metabolic rate, burning up fuel reserves.

Just as importantly, it may mean your partner, working a serious MVA at 3:00 A.M. in January, will develop serious hypothermia during the call. His metabolic rate was increased by the active shift, fueled further by his intake of caffeine to ward off exhaustion. The busy shift has not been conducive to good nutrition, so "dinner" was some tortilla chips grabbed from the hospital vending machine while clearing from the last call. Now your partner is in greater need of care than the patient he is trying to extricate.

4. **Explain thermoregulation.** Heat loss is a significant problem on every trauma scene, regardless of ambient temperature or time of year. Maintaining the patient's normal body temperature sounds like common sense, but it is easier said than done. The most diligent care providers can lose sense of their patient's environment and potential heat loss, depending on how hard they themselves are working during the call.

Explain the following principles of thermodynamics and their effects on the patient's thermoregulation:

   a. Evaporation—Almost all patients present with diaphoresis. The moisture on the skin encourages cooling, as well as fluid loss, which will exacerbate heat loss.

   b. Convection—Most trauma scenes are outdoors, so air currents are likely. Explain that the combination of evaporation and convection results in a fourfold loss of heat, not twofold, since the cooling mechanisms result in exponential worsening.

c. Conduction—Direct contact with the street, the sidewalk, or the garage floor, leads to conductive heat loss, which is then exacerbated by immobilization against the cold backboard, scoop, or stretcher.

d. Radiation—All humans lose radiant heat readily in our arid environment.

e. Conclusion—In the already vasodilated and/or hypovolemic patient, these factors combine to create a precarious situation with a real risk for hypothermia. Less often encountered, but just as dangerous, is the risk for hyperthermia due to excessive fluid loss through sweating and heat exposure.

CHAPTER 19

The Urinary System

INTRODUCTION

> What is man, but an ingenious machine designed to turn, with infinite
> artfulness, the red wine of Shiraz into urine.
>
> —Isak Dinessen

Acute problems of the kidney are not often an EMS concern. However, the many essential functions of the kidney form the foundation on which homeostasis is built. Hence, chronic malfunctions of the kidney and the syndromes they create provide the basis for many EMS complaints.

LECTURE NOTES AND TEACHING STRATEGIES

1. **Review kidney physiology.** Stress first and foremost the huge challenge the kidneys face in cleansing of the blood. Their combined weight is less than a pound, yet they filter almost 2000 liters of blood per day, with about 25 percent of the total blood volume being filtered at any given point. Should one kidney be lost to disease, trauma, or transplant to another person, a single kidney would be able to handle this workload after a brief period of massive growth for compensation.

   Explain that the kidneys' function makes them vital organs, and the body will maintain perfusion here as long as possible in times of blood or volume loss. A systolic pressure of at least 60 mmHg. is required for the filtration process. A trauma or shock patient who even transiently had lowered blood pressure to the kidneys may suffer acute renal failure following the initial accident. Emphasize this as yet another reason why supporting adequate perfusion must be a hallmark of emergency medical care.

2. **Discuss kidney anatomy and patient assessment.** The floating ribs and a significant fat layer surrounding them protect the kidneys, as does being covered by supporting fibrous connective tissue. Ironically however, lacerations by these same ribs pose a risk. The kidneys are located behind the peritoneal wall, which can make assessment difficult.

   Note that acute pain from the kidneys will be referred to the patient's lateral posterior aspect, or flank. However, chronic renal pain will eventually be referred to the anterior abdomen as well, as irritation of the peritoneum progresses. Complaints involving urination (dysuria, hematuria) should be assumed to be at the level of the kidney until proven otherwise. While blood, calculi, colic, and other pathologies can occur anywhere in the urinary system, instruct students to assume the worst and start by assessing the kidneys as the cause.

3. **Explain the kidney's involvement in hormonal disorders.** Review hormone secretion by the kidneys as discussed in Chapter 11, The Endocrine System. Describe in detail the mechanisms for precise autoregulation by the juxtaglomerular apparatus. Both erythropoietin and renin are secreted here. The kidneys therefore control both systemic perfusion to support the body and renal perfusion, to ensure adequate blood flow reaches the kidneys for efficient filtration. The so-called ACE-inhibitor (<u>a</u>ngiotensin <u>c</u>onverting <u>e</u>nzyme) medications have been successfully proven in treating hypertension, since they block the chain-reaction conversion of renin to angiotensin.

   Point out that alcohol and caffeine block the normal function of antidiuretic hormone at the nephron, allowing the kidney to excrete more water than normal. Patients with either or both of these chemicals on board may be potentially dehydrated. When ADH is either insufficiently secreted or inappropriately recognized at the receptor, diabetes insipidus can create dangerous dehydration.

   Discuss excess glucose. All blood glucose should be reabsorbed in a normal patient;

however, when blood glucose levels are exceedingly high, excess glucose is lost in the urine. Accompanying it will be copious amounts of water. It is this polyuria coupled with glucosuria upon which the diagnosis of diabetes mellitus is made.

Explain why so many chronic diseases, such as hypertension, sickle cell anemia, and diabetes, can do significant kidney damage. Autoimmune disorders, such as lupus, can also drastically affect this system, as supportive connective tissue is destroyed.

4. **Describe EMS treatment of kidney failure and dialysis patients.** A very common occurrence in EMS is being dispatched to a patient crisis at the local dialysis center. These can be some of the most challenging patients the paramedic will ever encounter. Explain the following factors in the management of these patients:

   a. Their medical history is extensive and complex, with a long list of accompanying medications.

   b. Depending on how much dialysis was performed prior to the 911 call, they can be either dangerously fluid overloaded or dehydrated.

   c. Their electrolyte levels can be grossly abnormal, making them vulnerable to a whole host of cardiac rhythm disturbances.

   d. Intravenous access may be very difficult, while the implanted shunt can be used only as an absolute last resort for venous access.

   e. The medics must provide supportive, vigilant care and prepare for resuscitation.

5. **Discuss acid-base balance.** Note the very narrow homeostatic pH range of the human body. The fact that our normal pH of 7.35–7. 45 is slightly alkaline while the cellular machine creates acids in large quantities seems counterintuitive. Explain that the cumulative effect is based on elaborate buffering mechanisms in both the respiratory and urinary systems. The respiratory system's role is instantaneous, but its capabilities are finite. Conversely, the kidney's buffering capacity is multifaceted and long-lasting. In

patient care, it is usually wise to err toward acidosis until exact data are obtained from an arterial blood gas sample. Aggressive airway management will correct many imbalances of the body's pH.

Point out that many physical conditions, both medical and traumatic, acute or chronic, can alter the body's pH. Therefore, EMS healthcare providers need to be knowledgeable enough in these syndromes to best manage them. Describe the acid-base balance disorders, as follows:

a. Respiratory acidosis—This the most commonly seen acid-base disturbance in acute situations, such as drug or alcohol overdose, chest trauma, and cardiac arrest. Hypoventilation, both in rate and/or loss of tidal volume, will create this type of acidosis. Carbon dioxide is not exhaled at its normal rate, and the increased carbonic acid accumulates in the blood stream, lowering the pH. Untreated, respiratory acidosis will lead to a more significant problem, as acidic waste products of metabolism amass. However, appropriate and aggressive airway management will reverse most acidosis, even when secondary to cardiac arrest.

b. Respiratory alkalosis—This occurs when CO_2 is overexhaled and carbonic acid concentration is decreased. It can be seen in prolonged asthma attacks, pulmonary embolus, high altitude, and extensive exercise in the inadequately conditioned athlete. Respiratory alkalosis, seen in hyperventilation syndrome secondary to anxiety is usually self-limiting.

c. The body also utilizes respiratory alkalosis to compensate for metabolic acidosis, such as Kussmaul's respirations seen in the diabetic ketoacidotic patient. Metabolic acidosis can also be secondary to shock, prolonged diarrhea, certain medications, and cardiac arrest.

d. Metabolic alkalosis—This is generally caused by renal failure, inappropriate use of diuretics, and prolonged emesis. It is also seen as an iatrogenic, or medically-induced condition, when sodium bicarbonate is administered in too large a volume for the accumulated acids.

CHAPTER 20

The Reproductive System

INTRODUCTION

The reproductive system causes only two main concerns for emergency care providers. (1) The assessment of these structures and their functions is emotional for all patients, regardless of age, gender, or situation. Social stigmas may cause embarrassment for both the patient and the care provider, potentially creating misdiagnosis or encouraging mistreatment. The consummate professionalism of the provider is key to easing this situation as much as possible. (2) The reproductive system gives rise to pregnancy and parturition—the only time paramedics start with one potentially critical patient who can become two or more such patients. This will be covered more fully in Chapter 21.

LECTURE NOTES AND TEACHING STRATEGIES

1. **Describe the male reproductive structures:**

    a. Discuss the testes/scrotum. These structures are externalized and therefore very vulnerable to injury. They are also highly sensitive, so that injury or irritation can be exquisitely painful. Explain that cold, pain, chronic illness, and other factors can cause the testes to ascend toward the abdomen as a protective feature, making their assessment difficult. The increased temperature of the abdomen also will decrease sperm production and motility, but this is not an EMS concern.

        (1) Explain that testicular cancer is relatively common, and not easily discernable by the patient; therefore, the diagnosis is delayed. It tends to metastasize to the lungs or brain, so the EMS call for respiratory distress, severe headache, seizures, or other CNS disturbances may mark

the initial assessment for the testicular cancer.

    (2)   Discuss testicular torsion. This is an acute emergency where the testes have become twisted within the scrotum. The supplying blood vessels also become kinked and obstructed, leading to potentially dangerous loss of vascular flow. This is most often seen in the teenage male. The pain is severe with sudden onset, and emergency surgery must often be performed to return the blood flow.

b. Discuss the penis. The penis is highly vascularized and dense in sensory nerve endings. Explain that injuries to the penis can be difficult to manage because the patient is highly emotional about the injury, bleeding can be difficult to control, and all movement is excruciating.

    Point out that sympathetic stimulation, such as that seen in shock or critical injury or illness, will block the erection mechanism, while priapism, or painful sustained erection, can be seen in spinal cord or head injury.

c. Describe the epididymis, ductus deferens, and seminal vesicles. Explain that these structures are less vulnerable to injury and infection due to their protected position within the pelvic cavity. Note the impossibility of determining the source of irritation from the outward signs of lower abdominal pain and/or painful/discolored urethral discharge. Fever may or may not accompany these signs and symptoms. Rapid transport with knees flexed will be the most appropriate care for this patient, with oxygen, IV, and monitor as needed.

2. Describe the female reproductive structures:

a. Explain that one of the most important history-related questions in the female patient is where she is in her menstrual cycle. This one fact will help greatly in the differential diagnosis for her complaint. Stress the importance of the paramedic's complete understanding of the timing and activities at each point of the menstrual cycle.

b. Discuss the ovaries. These structures are susceptible to acute or chronic conditions, and cancer. Protected within the pelvic cavity, they are less vulnerable to trauma.

   Explain mittelschmerz. Most women complain of "middle pain" at some point in their childbearing years. It is believed to be the pain of ovulation, as the follicle releases the ovum, although the ovaries have few sensory nerve fibers. Note that the patient may or may not have a history of previous episodes. Stress that vague, cramping pain on one side of the lower abdomen during the middle of the patient's cycle may be attributed to mittelschmerz but might also indicate more dangerous concerns, such as ectopic pregnancy or ovarian cyst rupture. As always in EMS, remind students to assume the worst and treat thoroughly.

c. Discuss the fallopian tubes. Explain ectopic pregnancy, a serious acute, potentially life-threatening condition. This is a fertilized ovum, or zygote, implanted and beginning development outside of the uterus. It most often occurs in the fallopian or uterine tubes, but can occur anywhere in the abdomen. Point out that a patient with a history of pelvic inflammatory disease (PID) or a significant sexually transmitted disease (STD) has a much greater risk for ectopic pregnancy due to damage and scarring of the fallopian tube. Review the menstrual cycle to remind students that an ectopic pregnancy can occur before the patient's menses is delayed, so that she may not even know she is pregnant.

d. Discuss the uterus. Describe the complex muscular development of the uterus as it allows for the efficient expulsion of endometrial lining each month during menses or of the fetus during parturition. Consequently, it is a highly vascular organ, as well. Discuss its vulnerability to injury in deceleration, blunt-force, or penetrating trauma, and explain that significant hemorrhage or rupture of the uterus can threaten the patient's life. Note that complications of pregnancy involving the uterus will be covered in Chapter 21.

e. Discuss the vagina. Explain that because it is constantly open to the environment, the vagina is susceptible to pathogenic infection and trauma from a variety of sources. Stress that while the assessment of these patients is critical, internal examination of the vagina should never be attempted in the prehospital environment. Should the patient be injured during a possible sexual assault, gentle external assessment should be given, checking for hemorrhage and for abraded or avulsed tissue or other injuries.

Special note about sexual assault: The EMS role in interactions with sexual assault patients is multifaceted. Any person of any age and any gender can be involved. Obviously, this is a highly emotionally charged scene where the medic's ability to quickly establish a compassionate, caring, yet professional rapport is essential.

Emphasize that care providers should not allow the patient to shower or to cleanse the affected body areas, including the hands, so that effective criminal data collection can take place later. Explain that discouraging the patient from washing will often take persistent yet gentle communication and that insisting on rapid transport may assist in this task. Explain that the medic's external assessment should be as brief as possible and utilize localized rather than direct pressure in hemorrhage. Medics should collect all patient clothing and belongings involved in the assault and take them to the hospital.

Discuss the importance of cooperating with law enforcement, as long as doing so does not obstruct or delay patient care. Point out that whenever possible using an EMS care provider who is the same sex as the patient will help with patient communication and cooperation. Remind students that the assault can involve multiple body systems, and stress the need to fully assess the patient, including head-to-toe evaluation, for other signs of injury. Medics must not let their own emotional response get in the way of adequate, thorough patient care.

3. **Discuss improper secretion of reproductive hormones:** Review the endocrine system's delicate control mechanisms, with hormones balancing each other. Explain that inappropriate secretion of sex hormones can also affect hormone balance systemically and exacerbate acute or chronic illness. Briefly discuss reproductive hormone imbalance as follows:

    a. Follicle-stimulating hormone (FSH)

        (1) Hyposecretion:

            (a)   Female: will cause improper maturation and release of ova from the follicle and inadequate production of estrogen. Follicle development may be improper, possibly giving rise to ovarian cyst formation.

            (b)   Male: can lead to inadequate or inappropriate sperm production.

        (2) Hypersecretion:

            (a)   Female: multiple ova can be developed and/or released, possibly leading to multiple-birth pregnancies. Follicles may develop too fast, releasing premature ova.

            (b)   Male: no known ill effects.

    b. Luteinizing hormone (LH)

        (1)   Hyposecretion:

            (a)   Female: improper formation of corpus luteum, from follicle, possibly leading to spontaneous abortions or preterm labor. Inappropriate development of follicle, potentially causing ovarian cysts.

      (b)   Male: altered function of the testicular interstitial cells, leading to inadequate or inappropriate testosterone secretion.

   (2)   Hypersecretion:

      (a)   Female: corpus luteum formation enhanced, giving rise to oversecretion of progesterone, which can alter pregnancy.

      (b)   Male: overproduction of testosterone from overactive interstitial cells.

c. Estrogens: (females only). Males are not vulnerable to inappropriate secretion of estrogen, although excess testosterone can be synthesized into estrogen in adipose and adrenal tissue, potentially creating female secondary sex characteristics. These effects can also be seen in men while ingesting anabolic steroids.

   (1)   Hyposecretion: poorly developed secondary sex characteristics, leads to inadequate secretion of LH, so the patient may have difficulty carrying pregnancy to term. Probable infertility. Has been linked to increased risk of cardiovascular disease in both genders.

   (2)   Hypersecretion: surplus estrogen converted to testosterone by adipose and adrenal tissue encourages male secondary sex characteristics, such as deepening of voice, body hair increase, and development of skeletal muscle mass.

d. Progestins: (females only).

   (1)   Hyposecretion: adequate progesterone levels are essential for pregnancy, so a significant decrease of progesterone, even temporarily, will cause spontaneous abortion, otherwise known as miscarriage. An interplay of progesterone and estrogen is required for a normal menstrual cycle, so inappropriate secretion of any involved hormone can cause irregular or

incomplete menses, leading to infertility.

    (2)   Hypersecretion: can deleteriously inhibit instigating hormone levels from the hypothalamus, disrupting FSH and LH, leading to inappropriate levels of all sex hormones. Overgrowth of endometrium may encourage uterine cancers.

  e. Androgens:

    (1)   Hyposecretion:

        (a)   Females: slowed bone growth-plate closure and inadequate skeletal muscle development.

        (b)   Males: inadequate development of secondary sex characteristics, immaturity of sperm production.

    (2)   Hypersecretion:

        (a)   Females: premature closure of epiphyseal growth plates and development of male-pattern baldness.

        (b)   Males: overactive development of sexual characteristics and behaviors. Has been theoretically linked to criminal sexual behaviors and aggression.

4. **Discuss reproduction and aging:** Note that massive amounts of data have been derived involving the hormonal changes after the reproductive years in both sexes and discuss the implications of this research:

  a. The decrease in estrogen after menopause has been linked to loss of bone density, osteoporosis, and increased cardiovascular disease and mental illness.

  b. Estrogen supplements possibly increase the risk of breast, uterine, and ovarian cancers.

  c. Decreases in circulating testosterone can alter heat and energy production in the aging male, making him more susceptible to heat and cold injuries.

d. As each generation becomes healthier and life spans increase, so does the time frame of normal reproduction. Menarche occurs earlier and menopause occurs later in life.

CHAPTER 21

Development and Inheritance

INTRODUCTION

Emergency medical services can be involved in the development of a new human being, from the first few days of pregnancy to the very end, due to the multiple complications that can occur. Also, in the age of the Human Genome Project, data are being gathered and knowledge is being assimilated regarding the genetic information contained in each human cell. Understanding the genetic information contained in each patient will aid treatment in every possible scenario. While EMS care will always be "in the trenches," the implications of this new knowledge base will have a huge impact on every area of medicine.

LECTURE NOTES AND TEACHING STRATEGIES

1. **Describe the challenges** of caring for the female patient who is having complications in a pregnancy. Not only are these calls emotionally demanding for both the patient and the care provider, but they also pose the potential for devastating risks to the mother's health, regardless of when in the pregnancy they occur. Also, this is the only time when care providers start with one potentially critical patient and then possibly finish with two or more.

2. **Discuss possible EMS-related pregnancy complications during the first trimester.**

    a. Define *ectopic pregnancy:* a pregnancy occurring outside the uterus. This most likely occurs within the fallopian tube, which can accommodate the fetal growth for only a few days. Explain that since no location other than the uterus can handle the substantial growth and vascular changes of the developing fetus, the risk is huge for damage, rupture, and hemorrhage wherever the fetus implants. Stress that medics should assume lower abdominal pain of any degree, with or without hemorrhage to be an ectopic pregnancy until proven otherwise.

b. Define *spontaneous abortion,* or *miscarriage*. Note that this can occur anytime in the pregnancy but is most likely during the first trimester. Explain that it usually represents the mother's body rejecting a fetus with congenital defects not conducive to life. Describe its usual presentation with cramping pain similar to, but much more severe than, usual menstrual cramps. Stress that any tissue expelled from the body needs to be preserved and transported to the hospital with the patient for further examination.

c. Discuss prolonged nausea and vomiting. Explain that while this is referred to merely as morning sickness, it can be unrelenting for some women. They can present with signs and symptoms of significant dehydration, including tachycardia, hypotension, and poor skin turgor. Proteins can begin to spill into the urine as the kidneys attempt to cope with the volume loss.

3. **Discuss possible EMS-related pregnancy complications during the second trimester:** Note that while this is usually when pregnancy is easiest on the mother-to-be, some complications can occur. Also note that placental abnormalities can present at any time during the pregnancy.

a. Define and explain *placenta previa.* If the placenta is implanted too low in the uterine cavity, covering the cervix, pressure from the rapidly growing fetus can damage it, causing vaginal hemorrhage. Note that hemorrhage from a placenta previa is painless, since no sensory nerve endings exist in the placenta. Obviously vaginal delivery is impossible in placenta previa, but it does not prevent the full-term pregnancy from continuing. Bed rest will be prescribed to take the fetus's weight off the placenta.

b. Define and discuss *placenta abruptio.* If the placenta is pulled prematurely from the uterine wall, massive hemorrhage with severe, tearing pain will ensue. This poses a potential life threat whenever it occurs during the pregnancy. Stress that the medic should never assume that an abruption always terminates the pregnancy.

c. Discuss orthopedic injuries/complaints. Explain that the hormone released by the placenta to soften the pubis symphysis and allow passage of the fetus during labor and delivery is not exclusive to this cartilage. It softens cartilages throughout the body, altering the articulations of all weight-bearing joints. Coupled with the mother's loss of coordination due to her rapidly changing weight and center of gravity, this causes new orthopedic complaints and exacerbates old injuries.

4. **Discuss possible EMS-related pregnancy complications during the third trimester.** Emphasize that any interaction with a patient during the last trimester of pregnancy should be assumed to include emergency delivery until proven otherwise. From 20 weeks of pregnancy and beyond, all trauma patients must be transported and thoroughly evaluated, no matter how insignificant their injuries may initially appear.

5. **Discuss the special concerns regarding blood loss and circulation** during pregnancy. Explain that by the end of the pregnancy, the mother will have 50 percent more blood than usual, but since she accumulates more plasma than erythrocytes, she will have the relative anemia of pregnancy. To compensate for this added blood volume, her blood vessels are more relaxed, giving a lower blood pressure. Her resting heart rate and respiratory rate, however, are higher than normal. Her uterus will have grown from approximately 3 inches long and weighing less than 2 ounces to 16 inches long and weighing up to 20 pounds; it contains the greatest amount of the extra blood. Given all these vascular changes, any blood lost in any from can have disastrous results. Further, two (or more) patients are now at risk, as both mother and child suffer from the lost

perfusion.

Also explain that from the end of the second trimester to the end of the pregnancy the uterus is large enough to compress the inferior vena cava and restrict blood return to the heart. Consequently, spinal immobilization must be especially secure, such that the backboard can be tilted to the side (preferably to the left, if possible) without any loss of integrity. Instruct students to avoid placing the pregnant patient into the supine position as she will often complain of dyspnea, as well as hypoperfusion, due to the uterus's compression of the vena cava and diaphragm.

6. **Discuss labor and delivery**. One of the most exhilarating and personally gratifying EMS calls is an emergency delivery. Since this is a rare occurrence in most EMS jurisdictions, medics do not get much practice. Encourage students to review emergency delivery techniques whenever possible, but point out that they should not be overly anxious about them. After all, women have been giving birth in teepees, rice paddies, and igloos for millions of years without EMTs, so emergency deliveries almost always occur without complications.

7. **Discuss congenital abnormalities.** Explain that defects in the genetic material of our cells and survival with significant congenital errors are both on the rise. This translates to the EMT having a greater chance of interacting with more patients who have congenital defects. These patients can be particularly challenging since their chronic care may involve high-tech medical devices not usually encountered by the EMT. Combined with the patient's in-depth, complex medical history, these devices can may make such calls seem overwhelming. Stress that these patients' family members are the medic's best resource, both for information and history, as well as for help with unfamiliar equipment. Note again that the Human Genome Project will yield amazing new information and insights and will affect all of medicine, including emergency medical services.